Life

BEGINNER

HELEN STEPHENSON

Australia · Brazil · Mexico · Singapore · United Kingdom · United States

Life Beginner Workbook
Helen Stephenson

Vice President, Editorial Director: John McHugh

Executive Editor: Sian Mavor

Publishing Consultant: Karen Spiller

Project Manager: Laura Brant

Development Editor: Liz Driscoll

Editorial Manager: Claire Merchant

Head of Strategic Marketing ELT: Charlotte Ellis

Senior Content Project Manager: Nick Ventullo

Manufacturing Buyer: Elaine Bevan

IP Analyst: Michelle McKenna

IP Project Manager: Carissa Poweleit

Cover: Lisa Trager

Text design: Vasiliki Christoforidou

Compositor: Lumina Datamatics Ltd.

Audio: Prolingua Productions and Tom Dick and Debbie Productions Ltd

Contributing Writer: Nick Kenny (IELTS practice test)

For product information and technology assistance, contact us at
Cengage Learning Customer & Sales Support, cengage.com/contact

For permission to use material from this text or product, submit all requests online **at cengage.com/permissions**
Further permissions questions can be emailed to
permissionrequest@cengage.com

ISBN: 978-1-337-28544-5

National Geographic Learning
Cheriton House, North Way, Andover, Hampshire, SP10 5BE
United Kingdom

National Geographic Learning, a Cengage Learning Company, has a mission to bring the world to the classroom and the classroom to life. With our English language programs, students learn about their world by experiencing it. Through our partnerships with National Geographic and TED Talks, they develop the language and skills they need to be successful global citizens and leaders.

Locate your local office at **international.cengage.com/region**

Visit National Geographic Learning online at **NGL.Cengage.com/ELT**

Visit our corporate website at **www.cengage.com**

CREDITS

Text: page 24: source: 'Immigration to Europe: how many foreign citizens live in each country?', Guardian News and Media Limited, 2016. http://www.guardian.co.uk/news/datablog/2010/sep/07/immigration-europe-foreign-citizens#; page 24: source: 'London, France's sixth biggest city', by Lucy Ash, BBC News, May 30, 2012. http://www.bbc.co.uk/news/magazine-18234930; page 24: source: 'Population of foreign citizens in the EU27 in 2009. Foreign citizens made up 6.4% of the EU27 population', Eurostat, September 7, 2010. http://ec.europa.eu/eurostat/documents/2995521/5051094/3-07092010-AP-EN.PDF/68b0c683-f8db-4918-aaf9-ffe74d68cfdc?version=1.0; page 88: 'Field Notes: Mike Horn', Nationalgeographic, 2007. http.//ngm.nationalgeographic.com.

Cover: © Miao Jian/Wuhan Morning Post/VCG/Getty Images.

Photos: 5 © Stephen Alvarez/National Geographic Creative; 7 (tl) © Christopher Meder/Shutterstock.com; 7 (tm) © Werner Buchel/Shutterstock.com; 7 (tr) © wavebreakmedia/Shutterstock.com; 7 (ml) © ittipon/Shutterstock.com; 7 (mm) © Jag_cz/Shutterstock.com; 7 (mr) © Denis Krasnoukhov/Shutterstock.com; 7 (bl) Mike Chepurin/Alamy Stock Photo; 7 (br) ONOKY - Photononstop/Alamy Stock Photo; 8 (l) © Phovoir/Shutterstock.com; 8 (m) © CREATISTA/Shutterstock.com; 8 (r) Paul Strawson/Alamy Stock Photo; 9 (tl) © 7th Son Studio/Shutterstock.com; 9 (tr) © Denis Krasnoukhov/Shutterstock.com; 9 (mtl) © Ben Schonewille/Shutterstock.com; 9 (mtr) © Bunwit Unseree/Shutterstock.com; 9 (mbl) © Jr images/Shutterstock.com; 9 (mbr) © Passakorn sakulphan/Shutterstock.com; 9 (bl) © FotosorokaShutterstock.com; 9 (br) © REDPIXEL.PL/Shutterstock.com; 10 © goodluz/Shutterstock.com; 13 frans lemmens/Alamy Stock Photo; 14 (l) © Jeremy Reddington/Shutterstock.com; 14 (r) © D.Bond/Shutterstock.com; 15 (l) © Mike Theiss/National Geographic Creative; 15 (r) © Nicole Duplaix/National Geographic Creative; 16 © dotshock/Shutterstock.com; 18 Elmtree Images/Alamy Stock Photo; 21 (tl, ml) © Featureflash Photo Agency/Shutterstock.com; 21 (tr) © leedsn/Shutterstock.com; 21 (mr) © Back Page Images/REX/Shutterstock; 21 (bl) © REX/Shutterstock; 21 (br) Image and Events/Alamy Stockphoto; 22 (tl) © Vitaly Korovin/Shutterstock.com; 22 (tr) © i viewfinder/Shutterstock.com; 22 (ml) © MSPT/Shutterstock.com; 22 (mr) © Igor Klimov/Shutterstock.com; 22 (bl) © Sebastian Studio/Shutterstock.com; 22 (br) © Zeynep Demir/Shutterstock.com; 23 © logoboom/Shutterstock.com; 24 Yuri Arcurs/Shutterstock.com; 25 (tl) ARISTO/Alamy Stock Photo; 25 (tr) © Songquan Deng/Shutterstock.com; 25 (bl) © Anneka/Shutterstock.com; 25 (br) © Jamie Grill/Getty Images; 28 (tl) Richard Levine/Alamy Stock Photo; 28 (tm) © LightField Studios/Shutterstock.com; 28 (tr) Richard Donovan/Alamy Stock Photo; 28 (mtl) Alex Segre/Alamy Stock Photo; 28 (mtr) Ian Dagnall/Alamy Stock Photo; 28 (mbl) Agencja Fotograficzna Caro/Alamy Stock Photo; 28 (mbm) © Jamie Wilson/Shutterstock.com; 28 (mbr) eddie linssen/Alamy Stock Photo; 28 (bl) © chaoss/Shutterstock.com; 28 (br) incamerastock/Alamy Stock Photo; 31 (t) Chris Lawrence Images/Alamy Stock Photo; 31 (b) © Michael Melford/National Geographic Creative; 32 © l i g h t p o e t/Shutterstock.com; 33 (t) © Vasca/Shutterstock.com; 33 (mt) © dan vojtech photographer/Shutterstock.com; 33 (mmt) © Layland Masuda/Shutterstock.com; 33 (m) © Evikka/Shutterstock.com; 33 (mmb) © stanislaff/Shutterstock.com; 33 (mb) © margouillat photo/Shutterstock.com; 33 (b) © Elena Elisseeva/Shutterstock.com; 34 © Luciano Mortula/Shutterstock.com; 36 (l) keith morris/Alamy Stock Photo; 36 (tr) © Andris Tkacenko/Shutterstock.com; 36 (mtr) © Peshkova/Shutterstock.com; 36 (mbr) © Fuse/Getty Images; 36 (br) © Joel Sartore/National Geographic Creative; 37 (t) © siamionau pavel/Shutterstock.com; 37 (mt) © Ljupco Smokovski/Shutterstock.com; 37 (mb) © l i g h t p o e t/Shutterstock.com; 37 (b) © Pressmaster/Shutterstock.com; 38 (tl, br) © Planner/Shutterstock.com; 38 (tml) © Zharinova Marina/Shutterstock.com; 38 (tmr) © irin-k/Shutterstock.com; 38 (tr) © Rob Wilson/Shutterstock.com; 38 (ml, bl) © Michael Cyran/Shutterstock.com; 38 (mml, bml) © MiloVad/Shutterstock.com; 38 (mmr, bm) © Evgeny Karandaev/Shutterstock.com; 38 (mr, bmr) © gcafotografia/Shutterstock.com; 39 © Everett Collection/Shutterstock.com; 40 © AP Photo/Danny Johnston/AP Images; 41 Radius Images/Alamy Stock Photo; 42 © Yuri Arcurs/Shutterstock.com; 44 © Peter Essick/National Geographic Creative; 46 (tl) Holger Burmeister/Alamy Stock Photo; 46 (tr) © T-Design/Shutterstock.com; 46 (ml) © Marvel Enterprises/The Kobal Collection; 46 (mr) © Minerva Studio/Shutterstock.com; 46 (bl) © Lisa S./Shutterstock.com; 46 (br) © Anan Kaewkhammul/Shutterstock.com; 47 Blend Images/Alamy Stock Photo; 48 TC/Alamy Stock Photo; 49 Asia Images Group Pte Ltd/Alamy Stock Photo; 53 © Joel Sartore/National Geographic Creative; 55 Mario Moreno/Alamy Stock Photo; 56 © maga/Shutterstock.com; 58 © Spike Mafford/Getty Images; 59 © Pascal Deloche/Getty Images; 60 © Blend Images/Shutterstock.com; 61 (tl) © Creativa Images/Shutterstock.com; 61 (tr) Blend Images/Alamy Stock Photo; 61 (ml) © Freebird7977/Shutterstock.com; 61 (mr) © LuckyImages/Shutterstock.com; 61 (bl) © kzenon/iStockphoto.com; 61 (br) Tetra Images/Alamy Stock Photo; 63 © Walter Bibikow/Getty Images; 64 © Maggie Steber/National Geographic Creative; 65 PhotoAlto/Alamy Stock Photo; 68 (l) Peter Cavanagh/Alamy Stock Photo; 68 (tr) © artproem/Shutterstock.com; 68 (mtr) © risteski goce/Shutterstock.com; 68 (mmtr) © sagir/Shutterstock.com; 68 (mmbr, mbr) © Karkas/Shutterstock.com; 68 (br) © Neirfy/Shutterstock.com; 69 © jgorzynik/Shutterstock.com; 71 ONOKY - Photononstop/Alamy Stock Photo; 72 © Joe Goodson/Shutterstock.com; 73 PHOTOINKE/Alamy Stock Photo; 74 © Jeremy Woodhouse/Getty Images; 76 © Wellcome Library, London; 77 © Topical Press Agency/Getty Images; 79 © New Line Cinema/The Kobal Collection; 80 INTERFOTO/Alamy Stock Photo; 82 © Sunghee.Kang/Shutterstock.com; 85 © Kenneth Geiger/National Geographic Creative; 86 © Eamonn M. McCormack / Stringer/Getty Images; 88 © Borge Ousland/National Geographic Creative; 89 © Eric Raptosh Photography/Getty Images; 90 © Sam Abell/National Geographic Creative; 92 © Randy Olson/National Geographic Creative; 96 (l) © Mark Yuill/Shutterstock.com; 96 (r) © Anna Baburkina/Shutterstock.com; 97 © g-stockstudio/Shutterstock.com.

Illustrations: 4, 5, 6 (t, b), 19 (m), 26 (t), 44 (3-5), 54 Lumina Datamatics Ltd.; 6 (mt, mb), 14, 29, 32 (map) David Russell; 8, 32 (clocks), 44 (1, 2), 56 Matthew Hams; 11, 12, 30, 52 (routines), 78 (scenes), 84, 94 James Gilleard/Folio Illustration; 16, 17, 19 (t, b), 32 (horizon), 40, 43, 48, 49, 52 (trees), 62 (whiteboard), 66, 67, 69, 70 (safe), 72, 78 (ill), 88, 99, 130 Laszlo Veres/Beehive Illustration; 20, 38, 57, 87 Alex Hedworth/Eye Candy Illustration; 26 (b) Norbert Sipos/Beehive Illustration; 62 (lecture), 70, 92 Peter Cornwell.

Printed in China by RR Donnelley
Print Number: 01   Print Year: 2018

Contents

Unit 1 Hello

1a People

Vocabulary the alphabet

1 💿 **1** Complete the alphabet. Listen and check.

Aa	....	**Cc**	....
Ee	....	**Gg**	....
Ii	....	**Kk**	....
Mm	....	**Oo**	....
Qq	....	**Ss**	....
Uu	....	**Ww**	....
Yy	....		

2 💿 **1** Listen again and repeat the alphabet.

3 💿 **2** Listen and circle the letter you hear.

1 A / (E)

2 E / I

3 G / J

4 H / J

5 K / Q

6 S / Z

7 Q / U

8 V / W

4 Say the letters. Circle the letter with the same sound.

1	A H J	(K) / T
2	B C D E	O / P
3	F L M	G / N
4	I	Y / Z
5	Q U	V / W

5 Dictation words

a 💿 **3** Listen and write the words.

1 .... *door* ....
2 ....
3 ....
4 ....
5 ....
6 ....

b 💿 **4** Look at the pictures. Listen and write the words.

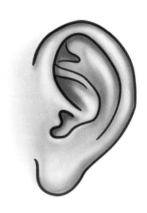

1 l _ _ _ _ _

2 l _ _ _

3 r _ _ _

4 r _ _ _ _ _

hello, hello, hello ...

Hello! I'm Dani.

Wri

5 s _ _

6 w _ _ _ _

Grammar *be*: *I + am, you + are*

6 Look at the photo. Choose the correct option.

'Hi. *I'm* / *You're* Louise Hose.'

7 Choose the correct option.

LOUISE: Hi. [1] *I'm* / *You're* Louise.

STEPHEN: Hello. [2] *I'm* / *You're* Stephen Alvarez.

LOUISE: Oh, [3] *I'm* / *you're* with *National Geographic*.

STEPHEN: Yes. Nice to meet you.

LOUISE: Nice to meet you too.

8 💿 **5** Write *I* or *You*. Listen and check.

1 Hi. _____'m Rosa.

Hello, Rosa.

2 Hello! _____'re Paul!

Yes! _____'m Paul Freeman.

3 Hello. _____'m Angela. _____'m a teacher.

Nice to meet you, Angela.

4 Hi. Nice to meet you.

Oh!, _____'re Jason Smith!

1b Around the world

Vocabulary countries and nationalities

1 Look at the maps. Write the countries.

1 the T U I D N E   *United*
  K I M N D O G   *Kingdom*
2 A S I S U R   ....
3 A I L T Y   ....
4 A I N P S   ....
5 A B I L R Z   ....
6 A A A C D N   ....
7 the I D T U N E   ....
  T E S T S A   ....
8 C E I M O X   ....
9 T E Y P G   ....

2 Pronunciation word stress

a 🔊 **6** Listen and circle the word you hear.

1 Russia / Russian

2 Egypt / Egyptian

3 Brazil / Brazilian

4 Canada / Canadian

5 Italy / Italian

6 Mexico / Mexican

7 Vietnam / Vietnamese

b 🔊 **7** Listen and repeat the country and nationality words from Exercise 2a.

Vocabulary numbers 1–10

3 Write the missing numbers.

a eight .... ten
b two .... four
c seven .... nine
d four .... six
e one .... three
f six .... eight

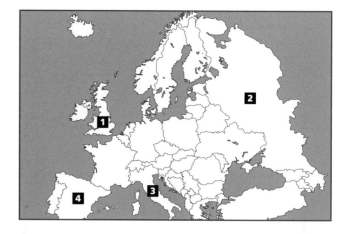

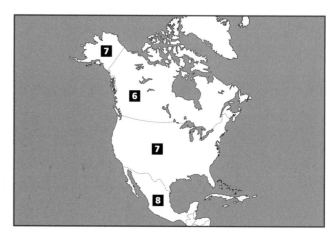

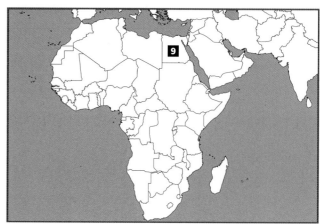

Grammar *be*: *he/she/it* + *is*

4 Write sentences with nationalities.

1 Anna is from Australia.
  She's Australian.

2 Jorge is from Brazil.

3 Cricket is from the United Kingdom.

4 Sâu is from Vietnam.

5 Pizza is from Italy.

6 Ahmed is from Egypt.

Listening an artist from Italy

5 🎧 **8** Look at the photo. Complete the text. Listen and check.

This [1] _____ Enzo Chellini. [2] _____ a painter. [3] _____ from Venice. Venice [4] _____ in Italy. Enzo [5] _____ Italian.

6 Dictation *be*

🎧 **9** Listen and complete the text.

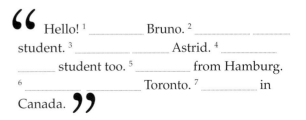

❝ Hello! [1] _____ Bruno. [2] _____ _____ student. [3] _____ _____ Astrid. [4] _____ _____ student too. [5] _____ from Hamburg. [6] _____ _____ Toronto. [7] _____ in Canada. ❞

1c Phone numbers

1 🔘 **10** Complete the greetings. Listen and check. Listen again and repeat.

1 Good_____ .

2 Good_____ .

3 Good_____ .

4 Good_____ .

2 🔘 **11** Complete the conversations with a–c. Listen and check.

   a And you

   b are you

   c See you

1
A: Good afternoon, Barbara. *How* _____ ?
B: *Fine, thanks.* _____ ?
A: I'm OK.

2
C: _____ *later*, Anna.
A: Bye, Carlos.

Listening phone numbers

3 🔘 **12** Look at the photos. Listen. Write the numbers (1–3).

Boris _____

Lisa _____

Nasser _____

4 🔘 **12** Listen again. Match the information in the table.

Name	Country	City
Lisa	Germany	London
Nasser	Mexico	New York
Boris	Egypt	Merida

5 🔘 **12** Listen again. Write the phone numbers.

Lisa   _____

Nasser _____

Boris   _____

Grammar *my, your*

6 🔘 **13** Complete the conversation with *my* and *your*. Listen and check.

LISA: Hi, Boris.

BORIS: Hi, Lisa.

LISA: What's [1]_____ phone number?

BORIS: [2]_____ mobile number is 707 839 116.
          [3]_____ work number is 707 547 939.

LISA: Thanks.

BORIS: What's [4]_____ home number?

LISA: [5]_____ home number is 55 018 375.

BORIS: Great. Thanks.

7 **Word focus extra *from***

Add *from* to three more sentences.
        from

1 Nasser is↑Egypt.

2 Joana is Madrid.

3 He's in London.

4 This phone call is Boris.

5 I'm Mexican.

6 He's South Africa.

1d What's this in English?

Vocabulary in the classroom

1 Write the names of the things.

1 p_____

2 c_____

3 c_____

4 b_____

5 n_____

6 p_____

7 t_____

8 p_____

Real life classroom language

2 🔊 **14** Write the words in the conversations. Listen and check.

down	home	late	open	page
repeat	spell	understand	what's	

1 S: _____ this in English?
  T: It's a computer.
  S: Thanks.

2 S: Good afternoon. Sorry I'm _____ .
  T: That's OK.

3 T: Work in pairs.
  S: I don't _____ .
  T: Work in pairs – two students.

4 T: OK. _____ your books. Look at _____ ten.
  S: _____ ten?
  T: Yes.

5 S: Can you _____ that, please?
  T: Yes. Look at page ten.

6 T: Good morning, everyone. Sit _____ , please.
  S: Good morning.

7 T: This is a table.
  S: Can you _____ it, please?
  T: T–A–B–L–E.

8 T: Do Exercise three at _____ . See you next time.
  S: Bye.

3 Pronunciation questions
🔊 **15** Listen and repeat the questions from Exercise 2.

4 Listen and respond questions
a 🔊 **15** Listen to the questions again. Respond with the sentences in Exercise 2.

> What's this in English?   It's a computer.

b 🔊 **15** Listen to the questions again. Respond with sentences about an object from Exercise 1.

1e My ID

Writing a visa

1 Writing skill capital letters (1)

a Rewrite the sentences with the correct capital letters.

1 my name is chris cavendish.
   My name is Chris Cavendish.

2 i'm from the united kingdom.

3 paula is from the united states.

4 spain is in europe.

5 alex robson is a doctor.

6 hanoi is in vietnam.

b 🔊 **16** Look at the table. Listen and write the words in the table. Write the correct capital letters.

a city	
a country	
a language	
a name	
a nationality	

2 Writing skill extra full stops, question marks

a Look at the examples.

What's your job⊘
I'm a doctor⊙

b Add full stops and question marks.

1 What's your name
2 It's 96 457 329
3 I'm fine
4 Can you spell that
5 My name's Chris Cavendish
6 Yes. C–A–V–E–N–D–I–S–H
7 How are you
8 What's your phone number

c 🔊 **17** Match the questions and answers in Exercise 2b. Listen and check.

1 ....
4 ....
7 ....
8 ....

3 Complete the visa form with the information. Use capital letters.

south african   writer   greta lessard

UK Visa

First name ....
Surname ....
Nationality ....
Job ....

Learning skills recording new words (1)

Write new vocabulary in your notebook.
Organize the words.

Countries

Brazil

South Africa

Vietnam

Italy

Russia

the United Kingdom

1 Write the words in three groups.

American   board   book   British   chair
computer   Egyptian   eight   five   four
Italian   nine   one   pen   pencil   seven
six   South African   Spanish   ten
three   two

Classroom objects	Nationalities	Numbers

Check!

2 Complete the sentences about you.

1 name
   My name's _____.

2 nationality
   I'm _____.

3 city
   I'm from _____.

4 country
   It's in _____.

3 Complete the crossword.

 (seven letters)

 (five letters)

 (seven letters)

 (five letters)

 (five letters)

 (five letters)

Unit 2 Holidays

2a My holiday

Vocabulary holiday places

1 Write the places.

1 a s e _____*sea*_____

2 a e k l _____

3 i c y t _____

4 a i d l n s _____

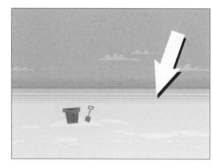

5 a e b c h _____

6 a i o u m n n t _____

Vocabulary days of the week

2 Write the days of the week.

1 S _ t ___ day _____
2 _ e _ n ___ day _____
3 T ___ e _ day _____
4 _ r _ day _____
5 _ h _ r _ day _____
6 _ o _ day _____
7 S ___ day _____

Reading my holiday

3 🔊 **18** Read the texts (a–c). Match the photo with one of the texts. Listen and check your answer.

a I'm on holiday. I'm with Friedl and Jane. We're in Africa. This is a mountain in Tanzania. It's beautiful.

b I'm on holiday. I'm with Linda, Will and Maria. They're my friends. We're in South America. This is Lake Titicaca. It's in Bolivia. It's beautiful.

c I'm on holiday. I'm with my friend, Jack. We're in Asia. This is on Phuket Beach. It's in Thailand. It's beautiful.

Grammar be: we/they + are

4 🔊 **19** Complete the sentences with *We're* and *They're*. Listen and check.

1 I'm on a beach. You're on a beach.
   _____*We're*_____ on a beach.

2 Andy is on a lake. Friedl is on a lake.
   _____ on a lake.

3 Friedl and Jane are Canadian.
   _____ Canadian.

4 Jane is English. I'm English.
   _____ English.

5 I'm with my friend.
   _____ in Fiji.

6 Jack is in Portugal with Michael.
   _____ in Portugal.

5 Pronunciation *we're, they're*

a 🔊 **19** Listen and repeat the sentences from Exercise 4.

b 🔊 **20** Listen and circle the word you hear.

1 (We're)/ They're from Portugal.
2 We're / They're in a city.
3 We're / They're Kenyan.
4 We're / They're on an island.
5 We're / They're in Canada.
6 We're / They're on Lake Titicaca.

Grammar be: negative forms

6 🔊 **21** Look at the photo again. Complete the sentences with the negative form of *be*. Listen and check.

1 This ____*isn't*____ in Europe.
2 I _____ in this photo.
3 The four tourists _____ Bolivian.
4 The man _____ a tourist.
5 We _____ in Thailand.
6 You _____ in this photo.

7 Pronunciation *isn't, aren't*

🔊 **21** Listen and repeat the sentences from Exercise 6.

8 Complete the blog about the photo with these words.

| aren't | holiday | my | they're | Wednesday |

Today is ¹ _____. I'm with ²
_____ friends. ³ _____ Linda,
Will and David. We're in South America.
We ⁴ _____ in Peru. We're in Bolivia.
We're on ⁵ _____. Lake Titicaca is
beautiful.

2b Is it hot?

Vocabulary numbers 11–100

1 Write the numbers in words.

   1 7 + 8 = _____ *fifteen* _____

   2 11 + 13 = _____

   3 19 + 28 = _____

   4 22 + 41 = _____

   5 17 + 59 = _____

   6 35 + 46 = _____

2 🎵 **22** Look at the weather information. Listen and complete the temperatures.

3 Look at the weather information. Write the temperatures in words.

   1 It's _____ *thirty-one* _____ degrees in Tokyo today.

   2 It's _____ degrees in London today.

   3 It's _____ degrees in New York today.

   4 It's _____ degrees in Mexico City today.

   5 It's _____ degrees in Rome today.

   6 It's _____ degrees in Santiago today.

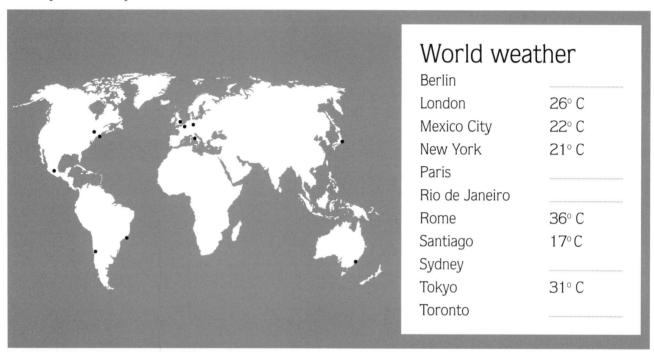

World weather

Berlin	
London	26° C
Mexico City	22° C
New York	21° C
Paris	
Rio de Janeiro	
Rome	36° C
Santiago	17° C
Sydney	
Tokyo	31° C
Toronto	

Berlin

Paris

Grammar *be*: questions and short answers

4 Look at the weather information. Answer the questions.

1 Is it hot in Sydney today?
No, it isn't.

2 Is it hot in New York today?

3 Is it cold in Tokyo today?

4 Is it hot in Rome today?

5 Is it cold in Santiago today?

6 Is it cold in Toronto today?

5 Read 1–8. Change the full stop (.) to a question mark (?) if necessary.

1 Are you in New York ?

2 John and Jane are in Rome.

3 Is she on the beach.

4 Are Paul and Meera in Santiago.

5 Your name is Andy.

6 Are you OK.

7 It is cold in London today.

8 Are they tourists.

6 Rewrite the questions from Exercise 5 as affirmative sentences. Use contractions if possible. Rewrite the sentences as questions.

1 *You're in New York.*

2

3

4

5

6

7

8

7 **Pronunciation *be*: questions and short answers**

💿 **23** Listen and repeat six questions and answers.

8 **Listen and respond *be*: questions and short answers**

💿 **24** Listen to the questions from Exercise 7. Respond with your own words.

1

Are you in London?

Yes, I am.

No, I'm not.

Rio de Janeiro

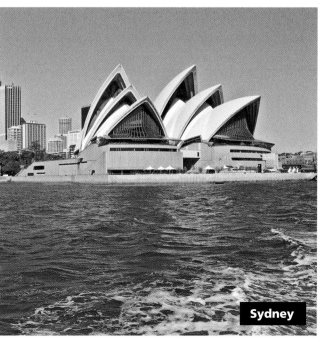
Sydney

2c Holiday places

Vocabulary colours

1 Write the colours.

1 a b c k l ....
2 a e g o n r ....
3 b o n r w ....
4 d e r ....
5 e b l u ....
6 e e g n r ....
7 e h i t w ....
8 e l l o w y ....
9 i k n p ....

Grammar *a/an*

2 Write *a* or *an*.

1 .... table
2 .... country
3 .... airport
4 .... page
5 .... island

3 **Word focus** *in*

Underline *in* in these questions. Then match the questions (1–3) with the answers (a–c).

1 What's this colour in English?
2 Are you in a hotel?
3 Are they in Tokyo?

a Yes, I am.
b It's 'orange'.
c No, they aren't.

4 **Dictation in New Zealand**

🔊 **25** Look at the photo. Listen and complete the email.

> Hi Stephanie
> I'm in New Zealand. It's ¹ .... The
> mountains are ² .... The sky isn't
> ³ .... – it's ⁴ ....
> I'm in a ⁵ .... I'm with my
> ⁶ .... Kiri. It's nice.

Glossary
the **sky** (noun) /skaɪ/

Grammar plural nouns

5 Write the plurals of these nouns.

1 bus ....
2 tent ....
3 car ....
4 city ....
5 office ....
6 photo ....

6 Complete the sentences with the singular and plural form of these nouns.

> beach   country   friend   hotel   island
> mountain

1 I'm on holiday with my .... Lynne and Felix.
2 Fiji is an .... in the South Pacific.
3 Nepal, China and India are .... in Asia.
4 We're in the Rocky .... in the United States.
5 I'm in a .... in London. It's old.
6 The .... in Australia are beautiful.

7 **Pronunciation plural nouns**

🔊 **26** Listen and repeat the plural nouns from Exercises 5 and 6.

2d Here are your keys

Vocabulary car hire

1 Look at a–f. Find:

1 two addresses
2 two email addresses
3 two car registration numbers

a *27 Front Street*

b mross@gmail.com

c WA 50 TCO

d 65 Liverpool Road

e *wilson@cars.co.uk*

f LE61 DGM

Real life personal information

2 🔊 **27** Complete the questions with *is, what* and *where*. Listen and check. <u>Underline</u> the answer you hear.

1 '_____ are you from?'
'I'm from *Belfast / Manchester.*'

2 '_____'s your address?'
'It's *27 Front Street / 65 Liverpool Road.*'

3 '_____ this your email address?'
'No, it isn't. It's *wilson@cars.co.uk / mross@gmail.com.*'

4 '_____'s the car registration number?'
'It's *LE61 DGM / WA50 TCO.*'

3 🔊 **28** Listen and complete the car hire form.

Title	Ms ▼
First name	Julia
Surname	Farrow
Address	
City	Manchester
Postcode	M19 2GR
Country	UK ▼
Email address	
Phone number	

4 Listen and respond personal information

a 🔊 **29** Listen to four questions. Respond with the information from Exercise 3.

1
Where are you from?

I'm from Manchester.

b 🔊 **29** Listen to the questions again. Respond with your own words.

1
Where are you from?

I'm from Jakarta.

5 Pronunciation syllables

🔊 **30** Listen and repeat these words. Count the syllables.

beach = 1

email   holiday   hotel   island   lake
mountain   number   student   teacher
telephone   tourist

2e Contact information

Writing a form

1 Writing skill capital letters (2)

a Rewrite the addresses (1–4) with the correct capital letters. Then match the addresses with a–d.

1   10 downing street
     london

2   221b baker street
     london

3   350 fifth avenue
     new york

4   1600 pennsylvania avenue
     washington

a   the Empire State Building
b   the President of the United States
c   the Prime Minister of Great Britain
d   Sherlock Holmes

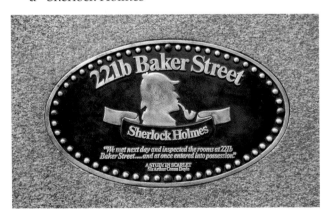

b Write the correct capital letters in this address.

ness hotel

loch road

inverness

iv4 2hf

c Rewrite the information in this form with the correct capital letters.

Ness Hotel online booking

Title	~~mr~~
First name	david
Surname	smith
Address	64 mill road
City	manchester
Postcode	m17 6rt
Country	uk
Contact number	0756 751 2587

Ness Hotel online booking

Title	*Mr*
First name	
Surname	
Address	
City	
Postcode	
Country	
Contact number	0756 751 2587

2 🔘 **31** Listen to the telephone conversation about a hotel booking at Lakeside Hotel. Complete the form.

Lakeside Hotel *booking*

Title	
First name	
Surname	
Address	
City	
Postcode	
Country	UK
Email address	
Contact number	0750 658 214

3 Check the capital letters in the form in Exercise 2.

Learning skills recording new words (2)

Write new vocabulary in your notebook. Draw the words or write examples.

car

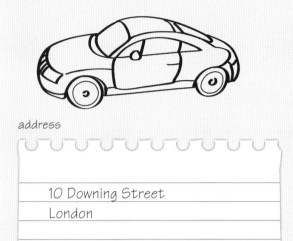

address

10 Downing Street
London

1 Match 1–4 with a–d.

a bus
b window
c ID card
d tent

2 Draw a picture or write examples for these words in your vocabulary notebook.

boat   country   city   key   mountain   tourist

Learning skills questions for the classroom and real life

3 Write these questions and expressions in your own language.

1 Can you repeat that?

2 Can you speak slowly?

3 How do you say … ?

4 How do you spell … ?

5 I'm sorry. I don't understand.

4 🔘 **32** Listen and repeat the questions and expressions from Exercise 3.

Check!

5 Look at the words. They are in Student's Book Unit 2. What are the connections? Look at the example. Then write four sentences.

1 *Gatwick and Heathrow are airports.*

2

3

4

5

brown **Cuba** Loch Ness
¹**Gatwick**
Cape Town
Fiji   **green**
¹Heathrow   **Moscow**
Paris Hawaii
red **Titicaca**

Unit 3 Family and friends

3a Families

Vocabulary family

1 🎵 **33** Look at the family tree. Complete the paragraph with these words. Listen and check.

> brother   father   mother   sister

66 Hi. My name's Jack. This is my family. This is Jamie. He's my ¹ _____ . This is Jenna. She's my ² _____ . This is Jane. She's my ³ _____ . And this is Jerry. He's my ⁴ _____ . We're from Ireland. 99

2 🎵 **34** Look at the family tree again. Complete the paragraph with these words. Listen and check.

> daughter   parents   sons

66 Hello. My name's Jane. This is Jenna. She's my ¹ _____ . These are my ² _____ , Jamie and Jack. My ³ _____ are Patrick and Moira. 99

3 Complete the sentences about the family tree.
1. Jerry and Jenna are ___*father*___ and ___*daughter*___ .
2. Jack and Jenna are _____ and _____ .
3. Patrick and Moira are _____ and _____ .
4. Moira and Jane are _____ and _____ .

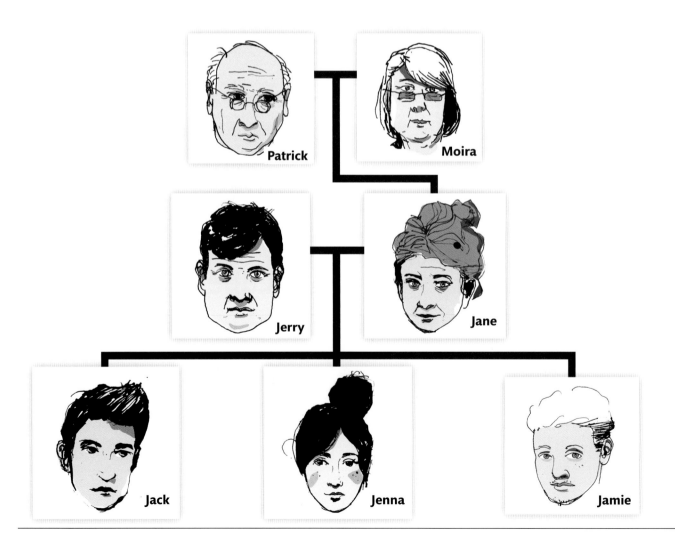

Patrick   Moira

Jerry   Jane

Jack   Jenna   Jamie

Grammar *his, her, its, our, their*

4 Read about the people. Complete the paragraphs with *his, her, its, our* and *their*.

1

Naomie Harris is from London. _____ mother is from Jamaica. _____ father is from Trinidad.

Naomie Harris, actress

2

I'm Sarah and this is my brother Mike. We're Australian. _____ parents are from a small town in New Zealand. _____ name is Dunedin.

Sarah and Mike Walker, artists

3

Arnold Schwarzenegger is Austrian and American. _____ parents are from Austria.

Arnold Schwarzenegger, actor and politician

4

Venus and Serena Williams are American. _____ parents are from the United States. _____ mother is from Michigan and _____ father is from Louisiana.

Venus and Serena Williams, tennis players

5

Emeli Sandé is from the United Kingdom. _____ mother is English and _____ father is from Zambia.

Emeli Sandé, singer

6

Mo Farah is British. _____ father is from the United Kingdom. _____ mother is from Somalia.

Mo Farah, athlete

5 **Grammar extra question words**

> **▶ QUESTION WORDS**
>
> **What's** your address?
> **When's** your birthday?
> **Where** are you from?
> **Who's** Naomie Harris?
> **How** old are you?

Look at the grammar box. Then complete the questions.

1 '_____'s Sarah's brother's name?'
  'His name's Mike.'
2 '_____'s Venus Williams?'
  'She's Serena's sister.'
3 '_____'s Emeli Sandé's birthday?'
  'It's in July.'
4 '_____ old is Mo Farah?'
  'He's thirty-four.'
5 '_____ is Naomie Harris's mother from?'
  'She's from Jamaica.'

3b Friends

Vocabulary people

1 🔊 **35** Listen and <u>underline</u> the word you hear.

1 <u>eyes</u> / hair

2 old / young

3 short / tall

4 old / young

5 eyes / hair

6 short / tall

Grammar possessive 's

2 Rewrite the sentences with the possessive 's.

1 Jane is Patrick classmate.
   Jane is Patrick's classmate.

2 Liam is my brother friend.

3 Who's Anne teacher?

4 What's Moira phone number?

5 Is this Jerry car?

6 Are you Liam best friend?

7 What's David surname?

3 Write sentences with the information.

1 Sol / eyes / brown
   Sol's eyes are brown.

2 Luigi / Kate / husband

3 Stan / hair / red

4 Jane / dad / not old

5 Carola and Marin / Bill / best friends

6 Rosa / sister / tall

7 Ed / surname / Smith

4 Look at the photos and the names. Write sentences with the possessive form.

Sarah

Eva

It's Sarah's notebook.

Ahmed

Felipe

5
Claude

6
Enzo

5 Find 's in the sentences. Write P (possessive 's) or *is*.

1 Who's Patrick?

2 Jack's family is from Ireland.

3 Anya's car is red.

4 She's my sister.

5 Is this your car? It's great.

6 Is your cousin's name Mike?

6 Pronunciation possessive 's

🔊 **36** Listen and repeat the sentences from Exercise 4.

Kate

Vocabulary ages

7 🔊 **37** Listen and complete the questions.

1 How old _____ ?
2 How old _____ ?
3 How old _____ ?
4 How old _____ ?

8 🔊 **37** Listen again and write the ages in words.

1 _____
2 _____
3 _____ : _____ and
   _____ :
4 _____

9 Read the names and ages. Complete the sentences.

1 Harry is 65. He's *Kate's father* .
2 Sam is 29. He's _____ .
3 Grace is 7. She's _____ .
4 Carol is 59. She's _____ .

10 Dictation possessive 's, contractions and plurals

a 🔊 **38** Listen and write the questions.

1 _____
2 _____
3 _____
4 _____
5 _____
6 _____

b Write your own answers to the questions in Exercise 10a.

1 _____
2 _____
3 _____
4 _____
5 _____
6 _____

3c People in Europe

Vocabulary months

1 Write the missing months.

1 January, February,
....

2 April, ... ,
June

3 .... ,
November, December

4 July, August,
....

2 Write the months with:

1 thirty days:
.... ,
.... ,
.... ,

2 thirty-one days:
.... ,
.... ,
.... ,
.... ,
.... ,
.... ,
.... ,

3 Listen and respond birthdays

39 Listen to four questions. Respond with your own words.

> When's your birthday?

> In February.

Grammar irregular plural nouns

4 Write the plural of these nouns.
Then write regular (R) or irregular (I).

1 child ....
2 country ....
3 family ....
4 man ....
5 person ....
6 woman ....

Reading and listening people in Europe

5 **40** Read and listen. Complete the article with these words.

| age | British | countries | five | old | young |

Europe

One big family?

In the United Kingdom, seven per cent of the people are not
¹ .... In Luxembourg, half of the people are not from
Luxembourg. They are from one hundred and seventy ² .... !
Forty per cent of the people are from the European Union (EU).

In Iceland, six per cent of the people are from EU countries. These people
are ³ .... The average ⁴ .... is thirty years old.

In Spain, ⁵ .... per cent of the people are from EU countries.
They aren't ⁶ .... The average age is thirty-two years old.

Glossary
average (adjective) /ˈævərɪdʒ/ usual

6 Word focus extra *on*

Add *on* to these sentences.

1 Look at the photo page 23.
2 My friends are holiday in London.
3 Is your English class Monday?
4 In this photo, we're a beach in Thailand.
5 The number is the key.
6 Bye. See you Friday!

3d Congratulations!

Vocabulary special occasions

1 Look at the photos. Write the occasions.

> a birthday   a new year
> a new baby   a wedding

1 _____

2 _____

3 _____

4 _____

Real life special occasions

2 🎵 **41** Complete the conversations with the expressions. Listen and check.

a   Congratulations!

b   Happy Birthday!

c   Happy New Year!

d   Here's a present for you.

1   A: _____
> B: Thank you!
> A: How old are you today?
> B: I'm ninety-five!
> A: Wow!

2   C: Twenty-one today!
> D: Yes, that's right. I'm twenty-one!
> C: _____
> D: Oh, thank you.

3   E: And this is Naomie.
> F: Ah, she's beautiful. _____ !
> E: Thank you. We're very happy.

4   G: Mum! Dad! _____ !
> M: And to you too!

3 Pronunciation intonation

🎵 **42** Listen and repeat three of the expressions from Exercise 2.

Real life giving and accepting presents

4 🎵 **43** Put the conversations in order. Listen and check.

1   a   Oh, thank you very much.

     b   You're welcome.

     c   Hello, Maria. This is for you and Oscar.

2   a   Oh, that's very kind.

     b   Hi, Daisy. Come in!

     c   This is for you.

5 Listen and respond special occasions and presents

🎵 **44** Listen to four sentences. Respond with your own words.

1

This is our new baby!

Congratulations!

3e Best wishes

Writing a greetings card

1 Writing skill contractions

💿 **45** Listen to six sentences. Listen for contractions. Write ✓ (contraction) or ✗ (no contraction).

1 ....   4 ....

2 ....   5 ....

3 ....   6 ....

2 Write the full forms of these contractions.

1 aren't ....

2 he's ....

3 I'm ....

4 isn't ....

5 they're ....

6 we're ....

7 what's ....

8 when's ....

9 who's ....

10 you're ....

3 Rewrite the sentences with contractions where possible.

1 What is his address?

....

2 It is not their car.

....

3 What are your names?

....

4 They are students.

....

5 How old are you?

....

6 What is your sister's name?

....

4 Write the card. Use these words. Check the capital letters.

> best wishes   from   happy birthday!
> laura and george   sandra   to

5 Write the card. Use these words. Check the capital letters.

> alex   congratulations   from   love
> martina and jeff   new son!   on
> to   your

Learning skills recording new words (3)

Here are three ways to record new words in sentences in your notebook.

- Write new words in a sentence.
- Write the word or sentence in your own language.
- Write a personal sentence.

tall	John is tall.
children	Son los hijos de Laura.
husband	My husband's name is Enzo.

1 Complete the sentences with these words.

classmates	eyes	men	old	present	
son					

1 Catalina, Petra and Jordi are my
_____ .
2 My parents aren't _____ .
3 What colour are her _____ ?
4 My _____ is six months old.
5 This is a _____ for your baby.
6 One man + one man + one man = three
_____ .

2 Look at these words from Student's Book Unit 3. Write sentences for the words.

1 hair

2 marathon

3 daughter

4 father

5 February

6 November

7 short

8 wife

9 women

10 young

Check!

3 Read the sentences about people in Workbook Unit 3. Write the words.

1 Sarah Walker is an _____
(T I S A R T).
2 Naomie Harris is an _____
(C E A S T R S).
3 Mo Farah is an _____
(H T T A L E E).
4 Emeli Sandé is a _____
(I G R S N E).

4 Read the sentences about people in Student's Book Unit 3. Write the words.

1 The two E O M N W on page 36 are friends.
_____

2 Andy and Jamie Murray are R S O E T B H R.
_____

3 The A I F L M Y on page 35 is from Iraq.
_____

4 The E I D G N D W on page 35 is in Baghdad.
_____

5 The N C E E L A T I O R B on page 39 is New Year.
_____

6 The S R N P O E with blue eyes on page 36 is Ana.
_____

5 Complete the crossword with the words from Exercise 4.

Unit 4 Cities

4a In the city

Vocabulary places in a town

1 Complete the places.

1 ba ___ ___

2 ca ___ ___

3 pa ___ ___

4 cin ___ ___ ___

5 ma ___ ___ ___

6 mu ___ ___ ___ ___

7 c ___ ___ pa ___ ___

8 b ___ ___ st ___ ___ ___ ___ ___

9 tra ___ ___ st ___ ___ ___ ___

10 inf ___ ___ ___ ___ ___ ___ ___ ___ ce ___ ___ ___

2 Complete the sentences with words from Exercise 1.

1 The Bois de Boulogne is a famous ___ in Paris.

2 *The Hobbit* is on at the ___ this week.

3 The Hermitage is a ___ of art and culture in St Petersburg.

4 My car is in this ___ .

3 Pronunciation extra words with *c*

a 🔊 46 Listen to these words. Is the *c* like *k* or *s*?

1 café ___

2 car park ___

3 centre ___

4 cinema ___

5 city ___

6 country ___

b 🔊 46 Listen again and repeat the words.

Listening asking about location

4 🔊 **47** Listen to four conversations. Where are the places? Circle the street.

1 Express Café   *Kent Street / Norfolk Street*
2 bus station   *Kent Street / Norfolk Street*
3 market   *Kent Street / Norfolk Street*
4 bank   *Kent Street / Norfolk Street*

5 🔊 **47** Listen again. Look at the map. Match the letters (a–d) with the places.

1 Express Café   ....
2 bus station   ....
3 market   ....
4 bank   ....

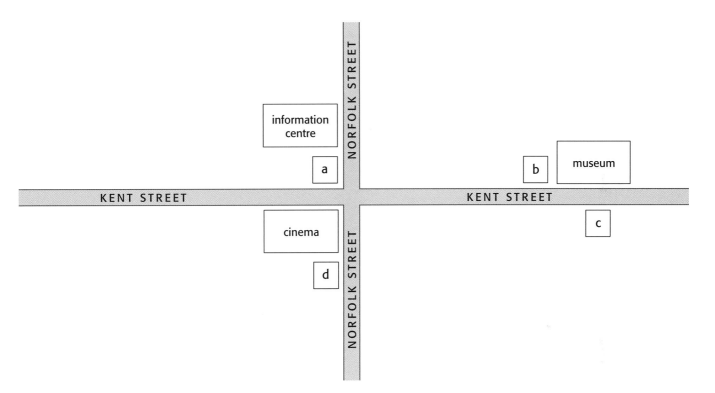

Grammar prepositions of place (1)

6 Look at the map again. Write sentences with the prepositions *in*, *near*, *next to* and *opposite*.

1 the information centre / Norfolk Street.
   The information centre is in Norfolk Street.

2 the bus station / Norfolk Street
   ....

3 the Express Café / the museum
   ....

4 the market / the Express Café
   ....

5 the information centre / the bank
   ....

6 cinema / the bank
   ....

7 Dictation prepositions of place

a 🔊 **48** Listen and write the sentences.

1 ....
2 ....
3 ....
4 ....

b Look at the map again. Are the sentences in Exercise 7a true (T) or false (F)?

8 Listen and respond asking about location

🔊 **49** Listen to four questions. Look at the map again. You are in the information centre. Respond with your own words.

1

> *Excuse me. Is the market near here?*

> *Yes, it is. It's in Kent Street.*

4b Tourist information

Grammar *this*, *that*, *these*, *those*

1 Look at the pictures. Complete the conversations with *this*, *that*, *these* or *those*.

1 ASSISTANT: Good afternoon.
TOURIST: Hi. Is _____ a timetable for trains to London?
ASSISTANT: Yes, it is.
TOURIST: Good. And are _____ times correct?
ASSISTANT: Yes, of course.

2 ASSISTANT: Good morning.
TOURIST: Hi. Is _____ a map of the city?
ASSISTANT: Yes, it is.
TOURIST: OK. And are _____ places near here?
ASSISTANT: Yes, they are. We're on this street, here.

2 Pronunciation *th* /ð/

a 🔊 **50** Listen and repeat these sentences.

1 The bank is open.
2 This is London.
3 That's the river.
4 See you there!
5 They're in Rome.
6 What are these?

b Add these words to the sentences in Exercise 2a. Write new sentences.

a map of	famous	next time	on holiday
today	timetables		

1 The _____
2 This _____
3 That's _____
4 See _____
5 They're _____
6 What _____

3 Vocabulary extra tourist information

Complete the sentences with these words.

~~bus~~	excuse me	guidebook	map	open
timetable	train			

1 This is the stop for the number 26 *bus* .
2 A _____ in Italian, please.
3 A _____ for trains to the airport, please.
4 _____ , is this Norfolk Road?
5 Here's a _____ of interesting tourist places.
6 Hi, is the café _____ ?
7 Is this the _____ to Oxford?

Reading tourist information

4 Read the information. Answer the questions.

1 What's the place?

2 Where is it?

3 Is it open on Monday?

THE OLD MARKET

The Old Market

Main Street

Alston

Open: Tuesday–Saturday 9–6

Sunday morning

Grammar question words

5 Match the two parts of the questions.

1 What   are we?
2 Where   is this building famous?
3 When   is this building?
4 Why   is the market open?

6 Look at the photo of a tourist. Where is she? Choose the correct option.

She's in *a street / a building*.

7 Put the words in order to make questions.

a is / where / that / ?

b it / when / open / is / ?

c open / it / today / is / ?

d map / on / it / the / is / ?

e of / this street / the name / is / what / ?

8 🔊 **51** Complete the conversation with the questions from Exercise 7. Listen and check.

WOMAN: Excuse me. [1] ....

MAN: It's Newbury Street.

WOMAN: OK. Thanks. Is the Old Market in this street?

MAN: No, it isn't. It's in Main Street.

WOMAN: [2] ....

MAN: It's in the centre of the village.

WOMAN: [3] ....

MAN: Yes … here.

WOMAN: Great. [4] ....

MAN: No, it isn't. Today's Monday.

WOMAN: [5] ....

MAN: Every day, but not Monday!

4c Time zones

Vocabulary the time

1 Look at the clocks. Write the times.

1 `09:25` *It's nine twenty-five.*

2 `10:15`

3 `12:30`

4 `17:20`

5 `18:10`

6 `20:45`

2 Listen and respond the time

🔊 **52** Listen to six questions. Look at the clocks. Respond with the times.

1

> What time is it, please?

> It's eight o'clock.

1 `08:00` 2 `11:30` 3 `09:15`
4 `14:45` 5 `16:00` 6 `10:20`

3 Dictation times and days

🔊 **53** Listen, and write the times and days.

1 The City Park is open every day from
.... to
....

2 The City Bank is open from ....
to .... It is open
from .... to
....

3 The Royal Cinema is open every day. It is
open from .... to
....

4 The Italia Café isn't open on ....

4 Word focus *at*

Choose the correct option.

1 Is your cousin *at* / *in* this photo?
2 I'm not *at* / *in* work today.
3 We're *at* / *in* a wedding.
4 Jane and Tom are *at* / *in* home today.
5 My friend's wedding is *at* / *in* Paris.

Listening and reading time in Ethiopia

5 🔊 **54** Listen and read about Ethiopia. Answer the questions.

1 Where is Ewan Jones?

....

2 Where is his office?

....

3 Is it the same time in London and Addis Ababa?

....

4 What are the two time systems in Ethiopia?

....

6 Read the article again. Label the clocks.

> East Africa Time   traditional Ethiopian time

a `13:00` Greenwich Mean Time

b `10:00` ....

c `16:00` ....

Ewan Jones is a scientist. He's in Addis Ababa. Addis Ababa is the capital of Ethiopia. Ewan's office is in London. It's midday in London (Greenwich Mean Time) and it's three o'clock in the afternoon in Addis Ababa (East Africa Time). But for some people in Ethiopia, it's nine o'clock – it's nine hours after sunrise. The traditional Ethiopian clock is twelve hours from sunrise to sunset, and twelve hours from sunset to sunrise. Midnight, East Africa Time is six o'clock in traditional Ethiopian time – six hours after sunset.

Glossary
sunrise (noun)
/ˈsʌnraɪz/

sunset (noun)
/ˈsʌnset/

4d Two teas, please

Vocabulary snacks

1 Complete the menu with these snacks.

> cake   coffee   fruit juice   mineral water
> salad   sandwich   tea

MENU

1 €1.50

2 €1.50

3 €3.00

4 €2.00

5 €1.50

6 €2.50

7 €2.50

Real life buying snacks

2 🔘 **55** Complete the conversations with the expressions. Listen and check.

1   a   No, thanks.
     b   Two cakes, please.

   A: Hi. Can I help you?
   C: ¹ _____
   A: Anything else?
   C: ² _____
   A: OK. Five euros, please.

2   a   No, thanks.
     b   Large.
     c   Can I have a coffee, please?

   A: Hi. Can I help you?
   C: ³ _____
   A: Large or small?
   C: ⁴ _____
   A: Anything else?
   C: ⁵ _____

3   a   Anything else?
     b   OK. Here you are. Eight euros, please.
     c   Can I help you?

   A: ⁶ _____
   C: A mineral water and two teas, please.
   A: ⁷ _____
   C: Yes. A fruit juice.
   A: ⁸ _____
   C: Here you are.

3 Pronunciation linking with *can*

🔘 **56** Listen and repeat these sentences with *can*.

1   Can I help you?
2   Can I have a coffee, please?

4 Listen and respond buying snacks

🔘 **57** Listen to the questions. Respond with the words.

1
> Can I help you?

> Can I have a coffee, please?

1   a coffee   4   small
2   two fruit juices   5   a sandwich
3   a mineral water   6   no

4e See you soon

Writing a text message

1 Writing skill *and*

Rewrite the sentences with *and*.

1 Our hotel is small. Our hotel is nice.
   Our hotel is small and nice.

2 Our hotel is near the old city. The hotel is near the sea.

3 The Grand Bazaar is old. The Grand Bazaar is famous.

4 The coffee's great. The food is great too.

5 The people are nice. The people are friendly.

6 The Topkapi Palace museum is great. The Hagia Sophia museum is great.

2 Match the pairs of sentences. Then rewrite the sentences with *and*.

1 It's hot here.
2 The museum is closed on Sunday.
3 The park is in Cambridge Street.
4 The town is beautiful.
5 The coffee is great.
6 The train station is old.

a It isn't open on Monday.
b It's sunny.
c Its centre is famous.
d The cakes are good too.
e It's beautiful too.
f The station is there too.

1 ....
2 ....
3 ....
4 ....
5 ....
6 ....

3 Complete the text message with these words.

and	great	hello	here	in	is
near	you				

1 .... from Turkey! We're
2 .... Istanbul! Our hotel is nice. It isn't big. It's 3 .... two museums – the Hagia Sophia museum 4 .... the Topkapi Palace museum. Istanbul 5 .... big!

The Grand Bazaar is a market 6 .... – it's old and famous. Oh, and the coffee's 7 ....!

See 8 .... soon.

Learning skills assess your progress

1 Complete the progress questionnaire for Units 1–4.

My progress in English: Units 1–4

❶ Tick (✓) the option that is true for you.

My progress in Units 1–4 is:

Excellent ☐   Good ☐   OK ☐   Not very good ☐

❷ Mark (↓) the place on the line for you.

	EASY	DIFFICULT
listening	EASY	DIFFICULT
reading	EASY	DIFFICULT
writing	EASY	DIFFICULT
spelling	EASY	DIFFICULT
speaking	EASY	DIFFICULT
pronunciation	EASY	DIFFICULT
grammar	EASY	DIFFICULT
vocabulary	EASY	DIFFICULT

❸ Complete the sentences for you with words from part 2.

I need to review:

Student's Book Units 1–4

....

Workbook Units 1–4

....

❹ What is your focus in Units 5–8? Write two words from part 2.

....

Check!

2 Find seven four-letter words and one six-letter word in the word square. Complete the sentences.

1 Excuse me. Is the market near

.... ?

2 Is .... London Road?

3 What's the .... of this street?

4 The car park is .... the bus station.

5 When is the bank .... ?

6 What .... is it?

7 Two cakes, ...

8 Can I .... you?

V	E	Y	P	L	E	A	S	E	E
O	T	L	E	N	E	B	X	Q	Y
N	H	Q	B	T	P	C	O	G	T
A	I	W	I	H	L	V	P	W	N
M	S	H	E	L	P	M	E	G	E
E	O	R	W	J	S	K	N	P	A
W	O	Y	I	J	D	O	S	L	R
B	I	U	O	Q	H	E	R	E	V
Y	T	I	M	E	V	L	T	A	I
O	A	Z	E	O	C	S	R	I	A

Unit 5 My things

5a Robots and people

Grammar *can/can't*

1 🔊 **58** Complete the sentences with *can* and *can't*. Listen and check.

Football with robots at the RoboCup in Singapore, June 2010

1 Look at the photo. This robot _____ play football.

2 Children _____ fly.

3 Babies _____ speak.

4 People _____ run.

5 Babies _____ see.

6 People _____ speak.

2 Pronunciation *can/can't*

a 🔊 **58** Listen and repeat the sentences from Exercise 1.

b 🔊 **59** Listen and circle *can* or *can't*.

1 *can / can't*

2 *can / can't*

3 *can / can't*

4 *can / can't*

5 *can / can't*

6 *can / can't*

Vocabulary abilities

3 Write the verbs.

cook	drive	play	play	ride	sing
speak	swim				

1 _____ the piano

2 _____ a car

3 _____ table tennis

4 _____

5 ....

6 .... a bike

7 ....

8 .... English

Grammar *can* questions and short answers

4 Look at the photos in Exercise 3 again. Then look at the example. Write questions with *can* for the photos.

1 you
   Can you play the piano?

2 you
   ....

3 your father
   ....

4 your sister
   ....

5 your mother
   ....

6 you
   ....

7 your brother
   ....

8 your friends
   ....

5 Complete the answers to the questions in Exercise 4.

1 No, ...
2 Yes, ...
3 No, ...
4 No, ...
5 Yes, ...
6 Yes, ...
7 No, ...
8 Yes, ...

6 Listen and respond abilities

🎧 **60** Listen to six questions. Respond with your own words.

1
   Can you speak English?

   Yes, I can.

5b Our things

Vocabulary possessions

1 Write the words.

1 a c m r

2 a c t

3 a f t b l

4 gl ss s

5 a g t r

6 a m t rb k

7 ph t s

8 a w tch

Grammar *have/has*

2 Look at the table. Are these sentences true (T) or false (F)?

1 Tatiana has photos.
2 Alvaro has a guitar.
3 Linzi and Jay have a motorbike.
4 Linzi and Jay have a camera.

					(camera)
Tatiana	✓				✓
Alvaro	✓		✓		
Linzi and Jay		✓		✓	
Boris	✓			✓	
Simona			✓		✓
John and Mimi				✓	✓

3 Look at the example. Write true sentences about the people.

1 *Tatiana has a motorbike and a camera.*

2 ....

3 ....

4 ....

5 ....

6 ....

4 Complete the sentences with *have* or *has*.

1 I .... three sisters.

2 My friend .... a VW car.

3 In my family, we .... two cats.

4 My sister .... four children.

5 My classmates .... dictionaries.

6 My brother .... a guitar and a piano.

5 Pronunciation *have/has*

💿 **61** Listen and repeat the sentences from Exercise 4.

6 Vocabulary extra adjectives and nouns

Write these words in the table.

bad	bag	battery	beautiful	expensive
family	famous	fantastic	friendly	
good	great	interesting	invention	new
nice	office	old	photo	robot	small
supermarket	young			

Adjective	Noun
bad	*bag*

Grammar *be* + adjective

7 Cross out the option that is not possible.

1 My bag is ~~bad~~ / *great* / *new*.

2 My family is *famous* / *fantastic* / *expensive*.

3 The supermarket is *expensive* / *small* / *young*.

4 Your friends are *big* / *nice* / *friendly*.

5 These robots are *famous* / *interesting* / *young*.

6 This photo is *big* / *friendly* / *old*.

Listening What's in your bag?

8 💿 **62** Listen to Raquel. Choose the correct option (a–c).

1 a a camera
   b a pencil
   c a watch

2 a books
   b glasses
   c photos

3 a keys
   b pencils
   c photos

4 a a photo
   b a phone
   c a watch

5 a a camera
   b a pen
   c a phone

5c Technology

Listening an unusual bike

1 Look at the bike in the photo. Why is it unusual? Choose the correct option (a–c).

  a It has three wheels.

  b It has pedals.

  c It has two water tanks.

1	a seat
2	a water tank
3	a wheel
4	a pedal

2 🔊 **63** Listen to a radio programme about the bike. Are the sentences true (T) or false (F)?

  1 The name of the bike is the Aquaduct bike.

  2 It can carry water.

  3 It has two small water tanks.

  4 It can make water clean.

  5 You can buy the bike online.

3 🔊 **63** Can you remember? Complete the sentences. Listen again and check.

The Aquaduct bike ¹ _____ a seat, pedals and three wheels. It has a ² _____ water tank and a ³ _____ water tank.

In a lot of places in the world, the water ⁴ _____ very clean. You ⁵ _____ drink it.

The Aquaduct bike is a really good idea for people in ⁶ _____ parts of the world.

Glossary
clean (adjective) /kliːn/
  the opposite of *dirty*

clean water   **dirty water**

Vocabulary technology

4 Write the words.

  1 a b e r t t y   _____

  2 a c a e m r   _____

  3 e m m o r y c i k s t   _____

  4 c e e n r s   _____

  5 a b c e m w   _____

  6 a d e e h h n o p s   _____

  7 a b e l t t   _____

  8 a l o p p t   _____

Grammar adjective + noun

5 Read the pairs of sentences. Write one new sentence.

  1 I have a phone. It's expensive.
     I have an expensive phone.

  2 These are glasses. They're grey.
     _____

  3 You have a car. It's white.
     _____

  4 My friend has a tablet. It's new.
     _____

  5 My phone has apps. They're great.
     _____

  6 I have a bag. It's small.
     _____

6 Word focus extra *of*

Add *of* to these sentences.

  1 What's the name this building?

  2 What's the capital France?

  3 Is that a map the city centre?

  4 This is a photo my family.

  5 I'm from the United States America.

5d How much is it?

Vocabulary money and prices

1 🔊 **64** Listen and match the prices with the money.

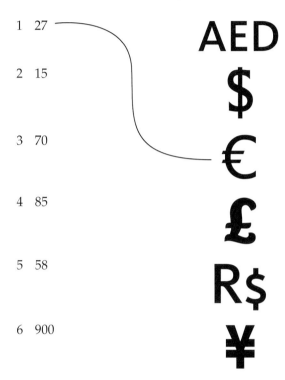

1 27

2 15

3 70

4 85

5 58

6 900

AED

$

€

£

R$

¥

2 Pronunciation numbers

a 🔊 **65** Listen and circle the price you hear.

1 £13.00	£30.00
2 £14.50	£40.50
3 £15.50	£16.60
4 £17.85	£70.85
5 £18.20	£80.20
6 £19.99	£90.99

b 🔊 **65** Listen again and repeat the prices.

3 Pronunciation extra /i/ and /iː/

a 🔊 **66** Listen and repeat these words.

fifty	is	it	sixty	stick	this	with
fourteen	please	seventeen	these			

b 🔊 **67** Listen and repeat these questions.

1 How much is this?
2 How much are these?
3 Is this sixty pounds?
4 Are these sixteen pounds?

Real life shopping

4 🔊 **68** Listen to a conversation in a shop. Answer the questions.

1 How much are the memory sticks?

2 How much is the camera?

3 Can the customer pay with a card?

5 🔊 **69** Put the words in order. Listen and check.

A: [1] I / help / you / can / ?

C: [2] much / these / are / how / speakers / ?

A: *They're forty-nine pounds.*
C: *OK.* [3] and / this / how / alarm clock / much / is / ?

A: *It's twelve ninety-five.*
C: *OK. I'd like this alarm clock and the speakers, please.*
A: *That's sixty-one ninety-five, please.*
C: [4] I / can / euros / pay / with / ?

A: *Yes, of course.*
C: [5] you / are / here / .

5e Can you help me?

Writing an email

1 Writing skill *but*

a Choose the correct option.

1 The camera is *good, but / good and* it's expensive.
2 I can *swim, but / swim and* I can't ride a bike.
3 The car is *great, but / great and* it's cheap.
4 Roberto can *cook, but / cook and* he can type.
5 My bike is *old, but / old and* it's fantastic.
6 This laptop has *a good screen, but / a good screen and* it has a keyboard.

b Rewrite the pairs of sentences with *but*.

1 She can speak English. She can't speak Italian.
   She can speak English, but she can't speak Italian.

2 My computer is new. My computer is very slow.
   ....

3 This phone is very basic. This phone is cheap.
   ....

4 This shop is big. This shop isn't very good.
   ....

5 I can ride a motorbike. I can't drive a car.
   ....

6 She can speak Russian. She can't write in Russian.
   ....

2 Read the email. <u>Underline</u> the three gadgets.

> Hi Mike
>
> I'm in a new job in London. My family is in Paris. I'd like a new phone with Skype or a laptop. I can't decide. (I have a computer in my job, but not at home.)
>
> Can you help me?
>
> Pascal

3 Match the two parts of the sentences.

1 Laptops are cheap, but
2 Laptops are cheap and
3 New phones are expensive,
4 New phones are expensive, but

a but Skype is cheap.
b they have cameras and MP3 players.
c they have a lot of programs.
d you can't carry a laptop in your pocket.

4 What is your answer to Pascal's question? Complete the email to Pascal with two sentences from Exercise 3.

> Hi Pascal
>
> ....
>
> ....
>
> Good luck in your new job!
>
> Mike

42

Learning skills learning new words

Vocabulary cards can help you learn new nouns and verbs.

a bike

1 Write the words. Write two nouns and one verb.

1 ....

2 ....

3 ....

2 Draw a picture for these words in your vocabulary notebook.

glasses   run   a keyboard

3 Make your own vocabulary cards.

1 Choose ten words (nouns and verbs) from Unit 5. Take ten cards. Draw a picture on one side. Write the word on the other side. Write *noun* or *verb*.

2 Take the ten cards. Look at the words. Can you remember the meaning?

3 Take the ten cards. Look at the pictures. Can you remember the words?

4 Look at five cards every day. Test yourself every week.

5 Organize the cards in different groups. Learn the cards in each group.

Check!

4 Complete the word puzzle.

1 It can play football, but it isn't a person. (Workbook page 36)

2 You can play music on this. (Workbook page 36)

3 You can ride this.

4 You can study in this place.

5 The money of Europe.

6 Andy Murray can play this game very well.

1					
2					
3					
4					
5					
6					

5 What is the word in the shaded squares? Write it here. ....

6a Sports

Vocabulary sports

1 Write the sports.

1 e i n n s t  ....

2 a a b b e k l l s t ....

3 g i i m m n s w ....

4 g i n n n r u ....

5 c c g i l n y ....

Grammar *like*

2 Look at the photo of a Canadian ice hockey team. Then look at the example. Complete their comments about sports.

1 ☺ ice hockey
   We like ice hockey.

2 ☹ football
   ....

3 ☹ cycling
   ....

4 ☺ tennis
   ....

5 ☹ basketball
   ....

6 ☺ swimming
   ....

Grammar *like* questions and short answers

3 Write questions and answers about the ice hockey team and the sports in Exercise 2.

1 Q: *Do they like ice hockey?*
  A: *Yes, they do.*

2 Q: ....
  A: ....

3 Q: ....
  A: ....

4 Q: ....
  A: ....

5 Q: ....
  A: ....

6 Q: ....
  A: ....

4 Pronunciation *do you … ?*

🎵 **70** Listen and repeat six questions about sport.

5 Listen and respond sports

🎵 **70** Listen to the questions from Exercise 4 again. Respond with your own words.

1
Do you like tennis?

Yes, I do.

No, I don't.

Vocabulary big numbers

6 Match the numbers.

a   500   eighty-eight thousand

b   9,000,000   five hundred

c   7,000   nine million

d   25,000,000   seven thousand

e   13,000   ten million

f   88,000   thirteen thousand

g   10,000,000   twenty-five million

7 🎵 **71** Listen and write the numbers you hear.

1   ....*300*...........

2   ....

3   ....

4   ....

5   ....

8 Word focus extra *it*

a Match 1–5 with a–e. Underline *it* in the sentences.

1   What time is it?

2   Is it hot in your city today?

3   What's your favourite place?

4   What day is it?

5   Hello, 9378675.

a   London. I love it.

b   It's ten o'clock.

c   It's Monday.

d   Hi, it's Susan.

e   No, it's cold.

b Write questions for the answers. Use the words in brackets.

1   (time)
    ....
    It's six thirty.

2   (how much)
    ....
    It's £25.00.

3   (day)
    ....
    It's Friday.

4   (hot)
    ....
    Yes, it's 35 degrees.

5   (football)
    ....
    Yes, I love it.

6b My favourite things

Vocabulary interests

1 Match the words with the photos.

| action films | birds | books | music | swimming | TV shows |

1 ....

2 ....

3 ....

4 ....

5 ....

6 ....

2 🔊 **72** Complete the comments with words from Exercise 1. Listen and check.

1 'I like animals. I like fish and ....'

2 'My favourite .... are wildlife and reality shows.'

3 'I like films, but I don't like .... I like comedies.'

4 'I like .... I like jazz and pop.'

5 'I like .... , but scuba diving is my favourite sport.'

6 'I have a lot of .... I like detective stories and novels.'

Listening favourite things

3 🔊 **73** Listen to an interview with Andrew about his favourite things. Complete the sentences.

1 Andrew's favourite kind of music is
....

2 Andrew's favourite TV shows are
....

3 Andrew's favourite detective is
....

4 🔊 **73** Listen again. Complete the table.

☺	☹
music – jazz	

Grammar *he/she + like*

5 Write sentences with the information from Exercise 4.

1 Andrew *likes jazz.* ....
2 He ....
3 ....
4 ....
5 ....
6 ....
7 ....
8 ....

6 Rewrite the sentences in the form given in brackets.

1 Andrew likes jazz. (question)
  Does Andrew like jazz?

2 Andrew's friend likes jazz. (negative)
  ....

3 Emile likes scuba diving. (question)
  ....

4 Emile likes novels. (negative)
  ....

5 Frances likes pop music. (negative)
  ....

6 Frances likes tennis. (question)
  ....

7 Pronunciation *likes, doesn't like*

🔊 **74** Listen and repeat six sentences.

8 Grammar extra *a lot, very much*

a Look at these questions and answers from the interview with Andrew Rollins.

I: *What's your favourite animal?*
A: *Oh, I don't like animals **very much**.*

I: *Do you like films?*
A: *Yes, I like comedies **a lot**.*

b Complete these sentences with the expressions in bold from Exercise 8a.

1 We use .... with *like* and *likes*.
2 We use .... with *don't like* and *doesn't like*.

c Put the words in order.

1 likes / Andrew / a lot / jazz
  ....

2 pop music / he / very much / like / doesn't
  ....

3 very much / tea / I / like / don't
  ....

4 like / sports / a lot / we
  ....

5 friend / very much / doesn't / my / like / TV
  ....

6 a lot / my / like / friends / films
  ....

6c The Paralympic games

Vocabulary food

1 Circle the food words.

birds	books	cheese	chocolate	colours
eggs	fish	friends	fruit	glasses	keys
meat	pasta	photos	rice	robots
salad	vegetables			

Reading and listening Jonnie Peacock

2 Look at the photo and read the text. Complete the sentences.

1 The Paralympic games is an _____ event.

2 The Paralympic games are every _____ years.

3 Jonnie Peacock is from _____ .

Jonnie Peacock and the Paralympics

The Paralympic games is an international sports event for disabled people. The Paralympic games are every four years. Jonnie Peacock is a British sportsman.

3 🔘 **75** Listen to a radio programme from the Olympic stadium. What is the programme? Choose the correct option (a–c).

a an interview with Jonnie Peacock

b a conversation with sports fans

c information about Jonnie Peacock

4 🔘 **75** Listen again. Choose the correct option (a–c).

1 About … people are in the stadium.

 a 8,000

 b 18,000

 c 80,000

2 Jonnie Peacock has … .

 a two artificial legs

 b an artificial leg and an artificial hand

 c one artificial leg

3 Peacock's event is the … race.

 a 100 metre

 b 200 metre

 c 400 metre

Glossary
artificial legs
(noun)
/ˌɑːtɪfɪʃəl 'legs/

a stadium
(noun)
/'steɪdɪəm/

Grammar object pronouns

5 Complete the sentences with object pronouns.

1 Jonnie Peacock loves running. He's passionate about _____ .

2 Jonnie Peacock is a great runner. I like _____ .

3 The people are in the stadium. Can you see _____ ?

4 A: Is that Ellie Simmonds?
 B: Yes, that's _____ .

5 Excuse me. Can I ask _____ a question?

6 Excuse me. Can you help _____ ?

6d Let's play table tennis

Vocabulary opinion adjectives

1 🎵 **76** Look at the pictures in the table and listen to the comments. Circle ☺ or ☹.

2 🎵 **76** Listen again and write the word you hear.

boring   fantastic   great   horrible

	Exercise 1	Exercise 2
1	☺ / ☹	....
2	☺ / ☹	....
3	☺ / ☹	....
4	☺ / ☹	....

3 Pronunciation intonation

🎵 **77** Listen and repeat the comments from Exercise 1.

4 Listen and respond opinions

🎵 **78** Listen to six questions and respond with your own opinion.

1 *Do you like steak?*

No, it's horrible.   *Yes, it's great.*

Real life suggestions

5 🎵 **79** Complete the conversations with these verbs. Listen and check.

don't like   don't like   have   like   love
play   watch

1 A: Let's ¹ _____ tennis this weekend.
   B: No, thanks. I ² _____ tennis. It's boring.

2 A: Do you ³ _____ action films?
   B: Yes, they're fantastic.
   A: OK, well let's ⁴ _____ *Die Hard* tonight.
   B: That's an old film.
   A: Yes, but it's great. I ⁵ _____ Bruce Willis.

3 A: Let's ⁶ _____ fish tonight.
   B: Oh, I ⁷ _____ fish. It's horrible.
   A: Well, how about pasta?
   B: That's a good idea.

6 Listen and respond suggestions

🎵 **80** Look at the conversations in Exercise 5 again. You are B. Listen and respond to A.

6e Can we meet on Sunday?

Writing short messages

1 Writing skill punctuation and sentence structure

a Read the conversations. Change the full stop (.) to an exclamation mark (!) in three places.

1 A: Is this film good?
   B: Yes, it is.

2 A: This film is boring.
   B: Oh. I think it's very good.

3 A: Do you like this singer?
   B: Yes, I do. She's fantastic.

4 A: My favourite sport is swimming.
   B: Yes, I like it too.

b Read the sentences and add the correct punctuation.

1 I have a new car I love it
   I have a new car. I love it!

2 no I can't come tonight.

3 do you like tennis I have two tickets

4 yes we love Italian food

5 let's go to the cinema

6 that's a great idea I love pizza

c Write the words in order. Add the correct punctuation.

1 come / you / for lunch / can / ?
   Can you come for lunch?

2 me / send / you / can / a message / ?

3 like / do / meat / they / ?

4 very much / fish / like / she / doesn't

5 time / you / come / what / can / ?

6 at 5.30 / English class / have / they / an

2 Writing skill extra pronouns

Replace the underlined words with the correct pronoun.

1 <u>This film</u> is very good.

2 He's really good in <u>this film</u>.

3 <u>The waiters</u> are really friendly.

4 I have all of <u>his films</u> on DVD.

5 <u>The singers</u> are fantastic!

6 <u>My friends and I</u> love Italian food.

3 Read the short messages. Write replies.

1 Can we meet tomorrow? It's important.

2 Do you like basketball? I have two tickets for the game on Saturday.

3 Are you at home? Can I phone you?

4 Do you like Tom Cruise? I have two films on DVD, but I don't like him.

Learning skills dictionaries

1 What can you find out from a dictionary? Tick (✓) the information you think is correct.

- the spelling of a word
- the irregular plural form of a word
- the meaning of a word
- the pronunciation of a word
- the stress of the syllables
- the type of word (noun, verb, adjective, etc.)

2 Can you answer these questions?

1 What's the plural of *woman*?

2 Is *bycycle* the correct spelling?

3 What does *festival* mean?

4 How do you pronounce *tonight*?

5 Where is the stress in the word *horrible*?

6 What type of word is *boring*?

3 Check your answers from Exercise 2 in these dictionary entries.

bicycle (n) /ˈbaɪsɪkəl/ a vehicle with two wheels, two pedals and a seat

boring (adj) /ˈbɔːrɪŋ/ not interesting

festival (n) /ˈfestɪvəl/ a special day or celebration

horrible (adj) /ˈhɒrɪbəl/ very bad

tonight (n) /təˈnaɪt/ the night of today

woman (n) /ˈwʊmən/ pl *women* an adult female

4 Look up these words in your dictionary or in an online dictionary. Find the information in Exercise 1.

digital   love   track   waiter

Check!

5 Find eight sports and food words in the word square.

B	I	H	T	F	U	I	F	O	J	X
L	C	H	E	E	S	E	F	O	Y	P
O	E	P	N	Q	E	P	O	Q	Q	E
E	Y	A	N	A	R	O	O	D	S	K
E	T	P	I	W	L	W	T	I	A	A
T	B	A	S	K	E	T	B	A	L	L
I	O	S	A	U	G	A	A	A	A	R
V	I	T	R	I	G	S	L	X	D	I
S	S	A	M	D	S	G	L	E	E	F
D	E	T	N	F	Z	H	I	B	T	L
V	E	G	E	T	A	B	L	E	S	W

6 Write sentences to give your opinion about the sports and food.

1
2
3
4
5
6
7
8

Unit 7 Daily life

7a Day and night

Vocabulary the seasons

1 Complete the words for the seasons.

a au_____n   b sp_____g   c su_____r   d wi_____r

2 Match the words from Exercise 1 (a–d) with the pictures (1–4).

1 _____   2 _____   3 _____   4 _____

Vocabulary routines

3 Look at the pictures and complete the expressions.

1   have _____

2   have _____

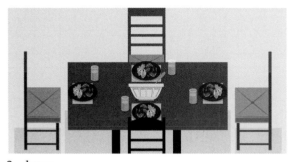

3   have _____

4   start / finish _____

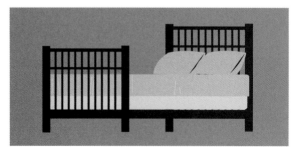

5   go to _____

Grammar present simple *I/you/we/you/they*

4 🔊 **81** Listen to Tommy and look at the information in the table. Tick (✓) the correct information.

	Tommy	Jeff and Bud
get up	5.30	6.00
have breakfast	–	5.30
start work	6.30	7.00
have lunch	12.00	13.00
finish work	17.30	15.30
go to bed	23.00	22.00

5 Read the sentences about Jeff and Bud. Rewrite the incorrect sentences.

1 They get up at five o'clock.

   They don't get up at five o'clock.

   They get up at six o'clock.

2 They have breakfast at half past five.

3 They start work at half past seven .

4 They have lunch at eleven o'clock.

5 They finish work at half past five.

6 They go to bed at eleven o'clock.

6 Pronunciation extra *don't*

a 🔊 **82** Listen and repeat these sentences.

1 I don't have breakfast.

2 They don't get up at five o'clock.

3 They don't have lunch at eleven o'clock.

4 They don't finish work at half past five.

b 🔊 **83** Listen and write the sentences. Are the sentences true for you?

1

2

3

4

5

6

Grammar prepositions of time

7 Complete the sentences with these prepositions.

> at   in   on

1 Jeff and Bud don't work ___ night.

2 We eat burgers ___ Saturdays.

3 We have breakfast ___ eight o'clock.

4 I get up ___ half past five.

5 You don't work ___ the evening.

6 I go to English classes ___ Monday, Wednesday and Friday.

7b Hobbies

Vocabulary hobbies

1 Look at the pictures and complete the words.

1   c _ _ _ _ ing   2   c _ _ _ ing

3   d _ _ _ ing   4   p _ _ _ _ ing

5   s _ _ _ _ ing   6   s _ _ _ ing

2 Which hobbies from Exercise 1 can you do in these places?

1   at home
2   in a town
3   outside

Reading A filmmaker from Zanzibar

3 Read an interview with Farouk. Are the sentences true (T) or false (F)?

1   Farouk is from Zanzibar.
2   Zanzibar is part of Tanzania.
3   The Zanzibar International Film Festival is in April.

> **a** I'm from Zanzibar. It's a group of islands in the Indian Ocean. It's part of Tanzania. About one million people live in Zanzibar.
>
> **b** We speak Kiswahili. I don't speak English very well, but I understand it.
>
> **c** My hobby is making videos. I have a YouTube channel about life in Zanzibar.
>
> **d** I make short films – about ten minutes. Each film is about one activity – fishing or building *dhow* boats or singing Taarab music. I think the culture of my island is very interesting.
>
> **e** I like films from other countries. Every July, I go to the Zanzibar International Film Festival. I learn a lot and the films give me ideas for my videos.

4 Read the interview again. Match the questions (1–5) with the answers (a–e).

1   Do you have a hobby?
2   Do you like films about culture?
3   What do your videos show?
4   What language do people speak in your country?
5   Where are you from?

Grammar present simple questions *I/you/we/you/they*

5 Write questions for Farouk with these words.

1 speak English

   Do you speak English?

2 live in Zanzibar

3 make videos

4 have a YouTube channel

5 like the culture of Zanzibar

6 enjoy the Zanzibar International Film Festival

6 Write questions with the words in brackets.

1 you / Kiswahili? (understand)

2 your friends / videos? (make)

3 we / an internet connection? (have)

4 your friends / to festivals? (go)

5 they / singing? (enjoy)

6 you / music? (listen to)

7 Write short answers for the questions in Exercise 6.

1

2

3

4

5

6

8 Pronunciation intonation in questions

🔊 **84** Listen and repeat the questions from Exercise 6.

9 Listen and respond

🔊 **84** Listen to six questions. Respond with your own words.

1

> Do you understand Kiswahili?

> Yes, I do.

> No, I don't.

7c You and the weather

Vocabulary weather

1 Look at the pictures and complete the sentences with a weather word.

1 It's very today.

....

2 I don't like days.

....

3 We have a lot of weather in winter.

....

4 I love  days.

....

5 Is it  today?

Listening you and the weather

2 Complete the sentences with these verbs.

cook	eat	~~meet~~	play	read	stay
take	watch				

1 In spring, I ___*meet*___ my friends at the park.
2 On sunny days, we _____ lunch outside.
3 We don't _____ TV very much in summer.
4 I don't like windy days. I _____ at home.
5 On rainy days, I _____ books a lot.
6 On rainy days, I _____ with my sister.
7 I don't _____ golf in winter.
8 I _____ a lot of photos in winter.

3 🎵 **85** Listen to interviews with three people. Tick (✓) the activities in Exercise 2 you hear.

Grammar present simple *Wh-* questions

4 Read the questions from the interviews in Exercise 3. Choose the correct option.

1 *When / What* do you do in summer?
2 *When / Who* do you watch TV?
3 *Where / Why* do you go on rainy days?
4 *Who / When* do you cook with?
5 *What / Why* do you like snowy weather?

5 Word focus extra *go*

Write these words in the correct places.

beach	cycling	outside	swimming
university			

go home
go ¹ _____

go for walks

go to the park
go to the ² _____

go climbing
go running
go skiing
go ³ _____
go ⁴ _____

go to school
go to work
go to ⁵ _____

7d What's the matter?

Vocabulary problems

1 Cross out the options that are not possible. Both options are possible in three sentences.

1 *I'm / It's* bored today.
2 *It's / We're* really wet!
3 *Are you / Is it* cold?
4 *I'm / It's* hot!
5 *Are you / Is it* hungry?
6 *It's / He's* tired.
7 *It's / We're* really thirsty!

Real life problems

2 🎵 **86** Complete the conversations with a–g. Listen and check.

a Are you OK
b Here you are
c I don't feel well
d I don't like tea
e I don't understand
f I'm thirsty
g Why don't you

1 A: What's the matter?
   B: ¹ _____ .
   A: Are you cold?
   B: No, I'm hot.
   A: Hmm.

2 C: What's the matter?
   D: I'm tired.
   C: ² _____
      go to bed?
   D: It's only nine o'clock!

3 E: ³ _____ ?
   F: No, I'm not. ⁴ _____ .
   E: Why don't you have a cup of tea?
   F: No, thanks. ⁵ _____ .
   E: Well, have a drink of water!

4 G: What's the matter?
   H: ⁶ _____
      this magazine article. It's in French.
   G: Why don't you use a dictionary?
   ⁷ _____ .
   H: Oh, thanks.

3 Pronunciation sentence stress

a 🎵 **87** Listen to these sentences. Look at the <u>underlined</u> words. Circle the stressed word.

1 I <u>don't feel</u> well.
2 I <u>don't like</u> tea.
3 I <u>don't</u> understand this <u>magazine</u> article.
4 Why <u>don't</u> you go to <u>bed</u>?
5 Why <u>don't</u> you have a cup of <u>tea</u>?
6 Why <u>don't</u> you use a <u>dictionary</u>?

b 🎵 **87** Listen again and repeat the sentences from Exercise 3a.

4 Listen and respond problems

🎵 **88** Listen to the comments. Respond with the words.

1 *I'm really thirsty.*

Why don't you have a cup of tea?

1 a cup of tea
2 a sandwich
3 a walk
4 a dictionary
5 bed

7e Meet our club members

Writing a profile

1 Look at the photo of Simon Woodford. Complete the sentences with these words.

cycling	Saturdays
cycling	teacher
married	two bikes
Pacific Technical College	two children

a I like ....

b I work at ....

c I'm ....

d I'm a ....

e We go .... in the mountains.

f We meet on ....

g I have .... – a boy and a girl.

h I have ....

2 Writing skill paragraphs

Look at the completed sentences (a–h) in Exercise 1. Organize them into three paragraphs:

1 professional information: .... , ...

2 family: .... , ...

3 interests: .... , ... , ... , ...

3 Complete the profile of Simon Woodford.

4 Writing skill extra capital letters (3)

> ▶ **CAPITAL LETTERS**
>
> We use capital letters
> - with languages
> - with days of the week
> - with months of the year
> - with names of schools, universities and companies
> - at the beginning of a sentence
> - for the pronoun *I*
>
> We don't use capital letters
> - with seasons

Rewrite the sentences so they are true for you. Check your capital letters.

1 i speak …

....

2 today is …

....

3 this month is …

....

4 my favourite season is …

....

5 i study/work at …

....

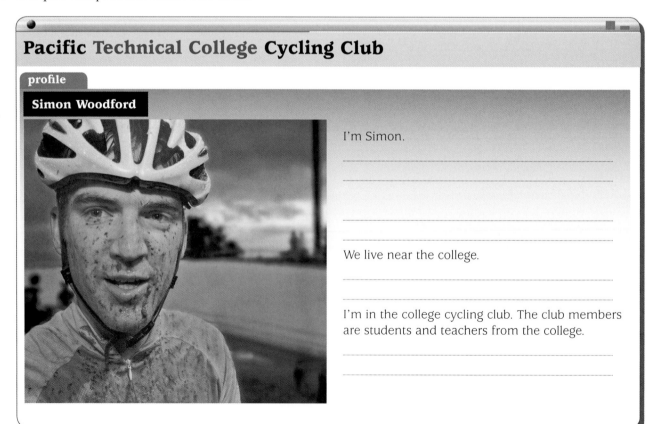

Pacific Technical College Cycling Club

profile

Simon Woodford

I'm Simon.

....

....

....

We live near the college.

....

I'm in the college cycling club. The club members are students and teachers from the college.

....

Learning skills study skills

1 When, where and how do you study? Tick (✓) the sentences that are true for you, or write a sentence of your own.

When?

- I study every day.
- I study two or three days a week.
- I do the Workbook exercises after every class.
- I don't study except in my English class.
- ....

Where?

- I study at home.
- I read my notes on the bus/train.
- I study in the library.
- ....

How?

- I meet friends and we practise English.
- I do the Workbook exercises at home.
- I do the Workbook exercises with my friends.
- I do extra exercises online.
- ....

2 Choose one new way of studying from Exercise 1. Try it for two weeks.

Check!

3 Read the clues and find the answers in Student's Book Unit 7 and Workbook Unit 7.

1   Zanzibar is in the ... Ocean. (six letters)

    ....

2   Is Whistler a good place to go in summer or winter? (six letters)

    ....

3   The ... is a kind of boat from Zanzibar. (four letters)

    ....

4   In this season, leaves go brown. (six letters)

    ....

5   A hobby with music. (seven letters)

    ....

6   What's the name of the spring festival in India? (four letters)

    ....

7   Where is British Columbia? (six letters)

    ....

8   Zanzibar and Shetland are groups of ... . (seven letters)

    ....

4 Write your answers from Exercise 3 in the spaces. Use capital letters. The letters connect the words. For example:

FESTIVAL + LESSON → FESTIVALESSON

1			I				

2					S				

3				A				

4			W				

Unit 8 Work and study

8a Friends and jobs

Vocabulary jobs

1 Complete the sentences about jobs with *in* and *with*.

1 Farmers work ___*with*___ animals.
2 Doctors work _____ hospitals.
3 Scientists work _____ laboratories.
4 Engineers work _____ modern technology.
5 Writers work _____ offices.
6 Filmmakers work _____ people.
7 Teachers work _____ schools.
8 Artists work _____ studios.

2 Listen and respond your job

🔊 **89** Listen to five questions. Respond with your own words about your job or your future job.

1

> *What do you do?*

> *I'm a scientist.*

> *I'm an engineer.*

Listening friends and jobs

3 🔊 **90** Listen to Amelia and Rajesh talk about Rajesh's friend Magnus. Are the sentences true (T) or false (F)?

1 Magnus has a new job.
2 Magnus lives in London.
3 Magnus drives a train.

4 🔊 **90** Listen again. Choose the correct option.

1 Magnus *writes / doesn't write* text messages.
2 Magnus *likes / doesn't like* his job.
3 Magnus *gets up / doesn't get up* early.
4 Magnus *drives / doesn't drive* a car at work.
5 Magnus *knows / doesn't know* a lot of people in London.

Grammar present simple *he/ she/it*

5 Complete the sentences about Rajesh and Amelia with the correct form of the verbs.

1 Rajesh ___*works*___ (work) in a hospital.
2 Rajesh _____ (enjoy) his job.
3 Rajesh _____ (not / sell) things in his job.
4 Amelia _____ (not / write) a lot of emails in her job.
5 Amelia _____ (not / watch) TV at work.
6 Amelia _____ (walk) to work in the morning.

6 Pronunciation -s and -es verb endings

a 🔊 **91** Listen and underline the verb you hear.

1 work / works
2 get up / gets up
3 start / starts
4 watch / watches
5 finish / finishes
6 go / goes

b 🔊 **91** Listen again and repeat the sentences.

Vocabulary job activities

7 Look at the photos and the letters. Complete the sentences with the jobs.

1   c d o o r t

A _____ talks to people and works in a hospital.

2   a e i r t w

A _____ works late.

3   a e g h h p p o o r r t

A _____ takes photos of people and places.

4   a i t x   d e i r r v

A _____ drives people on short trips.

5   e e i i o c n p r s t t

A _____ talks to people on the phone.

6   o h p s   a a i n s s s t t

A _____ talks to customers in a shop.

8 Dictation routines

a 🔊 **92** Listen and complete the sentences about these people at a London hospital.

1   Pauline _____

2   Amelia _____

3   Lisa _____

4   Kris _____

5   Jamal _____

6   Bill _____

b Rewrite the sentences from Exercise 8a. Change affirmative verbs to negative and negative verbs to affirmative.

1   Pauline _____

2   Amelia _____

3   Lisa _____

4   Kris _____

5   Jamal _____

6   Bill _____

8b School life

Vocabulary education

1 Look at the picture. Write the words (1–6). Then complete the caption.

1 t........................
2 b........................
3 s........................
4 p........................
5 b........................
6 p........................

A c........................ in a university

2 🎵 **93** Listen and follow the instructions.

In square one, draw a board.

1	2	3
4	5	6
7	8	9

Grammar present simple questions *he/she/it*

3 Look at the photo of Majed, Zahid and Tarik, three students from Oman. Write questions with the words.

1 Majed / go / to college?

   Does Majed go to college?

2 Tarik / live / in the capital?

3 Zahid / like / his school?

4 the school / open / every day?

5 Majed / study / English?

6 Tarik / have / classes in English?

4 🔊 **94** Listen and check your questions from Exercise 3.

5 🔊 **94** Listen again and <u>underline</u> the correct answer.

1 Yes, he does. / No, he doesn't.

2 Yes, he does. / No, he doesn't.

3 Yes, he does. / No, he doesn't.

4 Yes, it does. / No, it doesn't.

5 Yes, he does. / No, he doesn't.

6 Yes, he does. / No, he doesn't.

6 Complete the conversation.

A: What [1] _____ you _____ (do)?

B: I teach art at the City High School. My wife [2] _____ (work) there too.

A: [3] _____ your wife _____ (do) the same job?

B: No, she [4] _____ . She teaches science.

A: [5] _____ you _____ (enjoy) your jobs?

B: Yes, we [6] _____ . But my wife [7] _____ (have) a lot of students. She also [8] _____ (help) students after school. Science is difficult! And she [9] _____ (give) her students a lot of homework.

7 Vocabulary extra verbs and nouns

Write a noun with each verb.

the board	a notebook
a book	a pen
a classmate	the teacher
college	

1 go to _____*college*_____

2 listen to _____

3 look at _____

4 read _____

5 talk to _____

6 write in _____

7 write with _____

8c 24/7

Reading and listening 24/7

1 Read Part 1 of *Life 24/7*. Who are the people in the photo?

2 🔊 **95** Read the questions (1–5) and answers (a–e) in Part 2. Match the answers with the questions. Listen and check.

Grammar frequency adverbs

3 Put the words in order to make sentences. Then <u>underline</u> the frequency adverbs.

1 sleep / I / for eight hours / usually

....

2 people / study / scientists / often

....

3 twelve hours / sometimes / work / police officers

....

4 at home / work / never / I

....

5 customers / always / talk to / shop assistants

....

4 **Word focus extra** *every*

Add *every* to these sentences.

1 She goes to work day.

2 Do you change your routine week?

3 We meet month.

4 I talk to my mother evening.

5 Does he work night?

6 We go to the beach Sunday in summer.

Life 24/7

Part 1

Today people live and work 24/7: twenty-four hours a day, seven days a week. People are tired. They don't sleep well. Charles Czeisler is a professor at Harvard Medical School. This is his 'sleep laboratory'. These scientists study how people sleep. The computer screens give the scientists information.

Part 2

1 Why do you study sleep?

2 How do you study sleep?

3 Do you do experiments?

4 What are the results with the different colours?

5 Is blue light good for a tired person at work?

a Because sleep is important. In some jobs, people work a lot of hours. For example, police officers often work twelve hours. They are tired at work. That isn't good. Or nurses change their work routine every week. They finish work and they're tired, but they can't sleep. We can help people, but we don't understand sleep well.

b Well, blue light usually wakes people up.

c People come to our laboratory. They sleep and we watch them.

d Possibly. We aren't sure. We don't understand how it works.

e Yes, we do. For example, we change the light. We use different colours of light – blue light, red light.

8d One moment, please

Real life on the phone

1 Complete the phone calls with the expressions. You can use some expressions more than once.

a   one moment
b   I'll call back later
c   I'm sorry
d   can I speak to
e   can I help you

1   R: Hello, Life Laboratories.
      1 _____ ?

    C: Good morning. 2 _____
        Mr Simpson, please?

    R: Yes, 3 _____ , please.

    C: Thank you.

2   R: Good morning, Life Laboratories.
      4 _____ ?

    C: Yes, 5 _____
        Susana Barros, please?

    R: 6 _____ .
        She doesn't work in the mornings.

    C: OK, thank you. 7 _____ .
        Goodbye.

    R: Goodbye.

2 🔊 **96** Listen and check your answers from Exercise 1.

3 Listen and respond on the phone

🔊 **97** Listen to the caller. Respond with the words.

1
> *Good afternoon. Can I speak to Mr Smith, please?*

> *I'm sorry, he doesn't work in the afternoons.*

1   ✗ – doesn't work in the afternoons
2   ✓
3   ✗ – with a customer
4   ✗ – in a meeting
5   ✗ – out of the office
6   ✓

4 Pronunciation /s/ and /z/

a 🔊 **98** Listen to these words. Is the *s* like *this* or *is*?

calls   colours   drives   experiments   has
journalists   laboratories   nurse   wakes
writes

b 🔊 **99** Listen and repeat these sentences.

1   My favourite colours are green and purple.
2   My friend drives a police car.
3   My sister has a new job.
4   We do experiments in the laboratory.
5   I'm a nurse at the local hospital.
6   My son wakes up at five o'clock.

8e My new job

Writing an email

1 Writing skill spelling: double letters

a 🔊 **100** Listen and write the words. Which words don't have double letters?

1	....	9	....
2	....	10	....
3	....	11	....
4	....	12	....
5	....	13	....
6	....	14	....
7	....	15	....
8	....	16	....

b Complete the sentences with words from Exercise 1a.

1 'What do you do?'
'I'm an ....'

2 'Do you study at .... ?'
'No, I don't. I'm at university.'

3 'What time do you have .... ?'
'At 7.30, but on Saturdays we sometimes eat at nine o'clock.'

4 'Do you .... get up early?'
'Yes, I always get up at 6.30.'

2 Grammar extra prepositions

> ▶ PREPOSITIONS
> We use some prepositions for both time and place.

a Look at the table. Write *time* and *place* in the correct places (1 and 2).

b Write these words in the correct places (3–6).

Italy	night	the morning	university

	1	2 ....
at	six o'clock 3	home 5 ....
in	July summer 4	London 6 .... Hill Street
on	Mondays	a beach
from	six o'clock	Panama
to	nine o'clock	Africa bed

3 Complete the email from Craig with a–g.

a   an Italian restaurant
b   get up late
c   have pizza or pasta
d   I'm a waiter
e   in the morning
f   on Mondays
g   the customers are usually tourists

> Hi Oscar
>
> How are you? Where are you? Are you in Italy? I'm in Portugal and I have a new job in ¹............... ! And no, I don't wash dishes – ²............... ! My boss speaks English and ³............... . It isn't difficult – they always ⁴............... !
> The restaurant is open from midday to one o'clock ⁵..............., so I usually work late and ⁶............... . I don't work ⁷..............., so let's talk on Skype. How about next week?
>
> Craig

Glossary
wash (verb) /wɒʃ/
dishes (noun) /dɪʃɪz/

4 Underline five words with double letters in the email.

5 Write a reply to Craig's email. Use these ideas.

in Italy	finish eight o'clock
boring, not difficult	in a call centre
new job too	talk nine o'clock

> Hi Craig
> Yes, ...
> ....
> ....
> ....
> Oscar

6 Read your email and check your spelling.

Learning skills assess your progress

1 Complete the progress questionnaire for Units 5–8.

My progress in English: Units 5–8

❶ Tick (✓) the option that is true for you.
My progress in Units 5–8 is:
Excellent ☐   Good ☐   OK ☐   Not very good ☐

❷ Mark (↓) the place on the line for you.

listening	EASY	DIFFICULT
reading	EASY	DIFFICULT
writing	EASY	DIFFICULT
spelling	EASY	DIFFICULT
speaking	EASY	DIFFICULT
pronunciation	EASY	DIFFICULT
grammar	EASY	DIFFICULT
vocabulary	EASY	DIFFICULT

❸ Complete the sentences for you with words from part 2.
I need to review:
Student's Book Units 5–8

....

Workbook Units 5–8

....

❹ What is your focus in Units 9–12? Write two words from part 2.

....

Check!

2 Read about Salma's day. Look at the pictures and write the words.

Salma's day

Salma usually gets up at seven o'clock. She has

1 .... She likes coffee

and she always has two cups. Salma is a

2 .... at an

animal hospital. Her favourite animals are

3 .... Salma has

4 .... at one o'clock.

She finishes work at five o'clock. On Mondays

she goes to an 5 ....

class. She has 6 ....

at home at eight thirty. In the evening, Salma

often watches a 7 ....

– she likes comedies. She sometimes goes to

8 .... at midnight.

Unit 9 Travel

9a *Travel 365*

Vocabulary clothes

1 Look at the girl's clothes in the photo. Choose the correct option.

1 a hat / a pair of shoes
2 a top / a scarf
3 a jacket / a skirt
4 a dress / a jumper
5 a pair of jeans / a pair of shorts

2 Look at the clothes in the girl's backpack. Match these words with the clothes.

a pair of boots	a coat
a pair of shoes	a shirt
a pair of trousers	a T-shirt

1 ....

2 ....

3 ....

4 ....

5 ....

6 ....

Listening *Travel 365*

Chichen Itza, Mexico

Travel 365

Chichen Itza, Mexico
A travel idea every day of the year.
This week: beaches, castles, shops and unusual buildings.

3 🔘 **101** Listen to a conversation about the *Travel 365* magazine. Look at the two lists and match the tourist attractions with the places.

Tourist attractions	Places
pyramids	Edinburgh
a castle	Indonesia
shops	Mexico
beaches	Russia
old buildings	South Africa
a prison	Tokyo

4 🔘 **101** Listen to the conversation again and answer the questions.

1 How many steps does Chichen Itza have?

2 Can you visit the castle in Edinburgh?

3 Where can you go scuba diving?

4 Is the prison on Robben Island famous?

Glossary
a **castle** (noun)
/ˈkɑːsəl/

a **prison** (noun)
/ˈprɪzən/

a **step** (noun)
/step/

Grammar *there is/are*

5 Complete the sentences about the places in Exercise 3 with *There's* and *There are*.

1 _____ some unusual pyramids in Mexico.

2 _____ an amazing castle in Edinburgh.

3 _____ some fantastic shops in Tokyo.

4 _____ some beautiful beaches in Indonesia.

5 _____ some beautiful old buildings in Russia.

6 _____ a famous prison in South Africa.

6 Pronunciation *there are*

🔘 **102** Listen and repeat four sentences from Exercise 5.

7 Pronunciation extra *they're* and *there*

a 🔘 **103** Listen to the pronunciation of *they're* and *there* in these sentences. Note how they sound the same.

1 There are some pyramids in Mexico.
   They're amazing.

2 There are some shops in Tokyo.
   They're fantastic.

3 There are some beaches in Indonesia.
   They're beautiful.

4 There are some beautiful buildings in Russia.
   They're old.

b 🔘 **104** Listen and repeat the sentences from Exercise 7a.

8 Dictation *they're* and *there*

🔘 **105** Listen and write the sentences about the speaker's suitcase.

1 _____
2 _____
3 _____
4 _____
5 _____
6 _____

9b Places to stay

Vocabulary hotel rooms

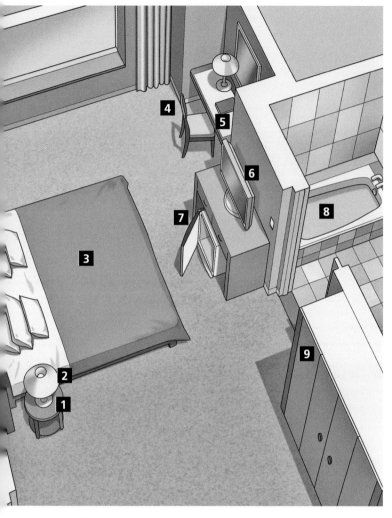

1 Match the words with the furniture in the hotel room. Which three things are not in the picture?

armchair   bath   bed   chair   desk
fridge   lamp   shower   sofa   table
TV   wardrobe

1 ....
2 ....
3 ....
4 ....
5 ....
6 ....
7 ....
8 ....
9 ....

not in the picture: .... ,

.... , ...

Reading Hotel Miramar

2 Read about the rooms in the Hotel Miramar. Look at the picture in Exercise 1. Choose the correct option.

The room in the picture is an *Executive* / *Superior* / *Club* room.

All our rooms have double beds and are very comfortable. Superior rooms have armchairs and a sofa so you can relax. There are TVs and fridges in all rooms. In our Executive rooms, there's a desk and a chair so you can work. There's a bathroom, with a bath and a shower, in all our rooms. There are ten Club rooms in the hotel. These rooms have a sea view.

	Executive	Superior	Club
sea view	–	–	✓
double bed	✓	✓	✓
sofa and armchairs	–	✓	✓
internet connection	✓	✓	✓
fridge	✓	✓	✓
TV	✓	✓	✓
DVD player	–	–	✓
drinks (hot and cold)	–	✓	✓
basket of fruit and chocolate	–	–	✓
safe	–	✓	✓
magazines	–	–	✓

Glossary
a **safe** (noun) /seɪf/

Grammar *there is/are* negative and question forms

3 Look at the information about the Hotel Miramar rooms. Write questions.

1 double bed / Club rooms
Is there a double bed in the Club rooms?

2 DVD player / Club rooms

3 magazines / Executive rooms

4 basket of fruit / Superior rooms

5 drinks / Executive rooms

6 fridge / Superior rooms

4 Look at the information about the Hotel Miramar rooms. Write the answers to the questions in Exercise 3.

1 *Yes, there is.*

2

3

4

5

6

5 Write sentences about the Hotel Miramar rooms.

1 sea view / Executive rooms
There isn't a sea view in the Executive rooms.

2 armchairs / Executive rooms

3 DVD player / Superior rooms

4 basket of fruit / Executive rooms

5 a safe / Executive rooms

6 magazines / Superior rooms

6 🔊 **106** Complete the conversation with the correct forms of *there is/are*. Use *any* if necessary. Listen and check.

A: The Hotel Miramar is nice.

B: Yes, but it's expensive. [1] _____ cheap hotels near the beach?

A: Yes, [2] _____ two or three. And [3] _____ a youth hostel too.

B: [4] _____ a website for the youth hostel?

A: Let's see. I don't think so. No, [5] _____. There's an email address and [6] _____ a phone number, but [7] _____ a website.

B: OK. What about that hotel – Golden Sands? [8] _____ a website?

A: Yes, [9] _____ – but [10] _____ free rooms.

B: Oh well. Let's send an email to the youth hostel.

7 Word focus extra *to*

a Read the conversation and underline *to*.

A: Let's go to Loch Ness for New Year.

B: Are there any flights from here?

A: Yes, there are. There are flights from Monday to Friday.

B: Really?

A: Yes. It's popular in winter – from December to February there are lots of flights.

B: OK.

A: And there's a bus from the airport to the hotel.

B: Great!

b Are these sentences true (T) or false (F)?

1 We use *to* with expressions for time.

2 We use *to* with expressions for places.

9c Road trips

Listening New Zealand road trip

1 🔊 **107** Listen to the information about a trip in New Zealand. Choose the correct option.

1	where?	the North Island / the South Island
2	how?	by bus / by car
3	distance?	470 kilometres / 740 kilometres
4	from / to?	Wellington – Auckland / Auckland – Wellington
5	places to stay?	bed and breakfast places / hotels

2 🔊 **107** Listen again. Are the sentences true (T) or false (F)?

1 You can drive from Auckland to Wellington in four days.
2 There's a museum in Auckland.
3 There aren't any volcanoes on the North Island.
4 Rotorua is a good place to visit.
5 People in New Zealand drive on the left of the road.

Glossary

a **bed and breakfast (B&B)** (noun) /ˌbed ən ˈbrekfəst/ a place to sleep – a private house

a **volcano** (noun) /vɒlˈkeɪnəʊ/

Vocabulary travel

3 Match the two parts of the sentences.

1 Do you often travel
2 I usually take
3 Lots of tourists visit
4 You can't drive
5 I often buy
6 You can't fly

a a taxi from the airport.
b by train?
c a car in this park.
d New Zealand every year.
e to this city – there isn't an airport.
f train tickets online.

4 Word focus extra *take*

Look at the questions a tourist asks a travel agent. Rewrite the questions with these words instead of the underlined words.

bus	suitcases	the plane

1 Can I take two <u>bags</u> on the plane?

....

2 Can I take photos in <u>passport control</u>?

....

3 Can I take a <u>train</u> to the airport?

....

Grammar imperative forms

5 Complete the tips for travellers in New Zealand. Use the affirmative and negative imperative form of these verbs.

drive	go	start	stay	visit

TIPS FOR TRAVELLERS

1 .... your trip in Auckland.
2 .... on the right.
3 .... in hotels.
4 .... the hot lakes in Rotorua.
5 .... on a *The Lord of the Rings* tour of Wellington.

9d At the hotel

Vocabulary hotels

1 Write the correct words.

café	restaurant
car park	swimming pool
gift shop	wi-fi

You want:

1 to have dinner

2 to go online

3 to go swimming

4 to leave your car

5 to buy a present

6 to have a cup of coffee

Real life requests

2 🔊 **108** Listen to three conversations between hotel guests and a receptionist. Choose the correct option (a–c).

1 Mr Khan would like a room for … .
   a one night
   b three nights
   c a week

2 The receptionist would like Mr Khan's … .
   a passport
   b credit card
   c phone number

3 Mr and Mrs Jones would like … .
   a a different room
   b a taxi
   c help with their bags

4 Mr Khan would like … .
   a a key
   b a snack
   c a password

3 🔊 **108** Listen to the conversations again. <u>Underline</u> the responses to requests you hear.

1 Certainly. / Of course.
2 Here you are. / Yes, please.
3 Just a moment. / Yes, of course.
4 That's fine. / That's no problem.

4 Pronunciation *I'd like, We'd like*

🔊 **109** Listen and repeat these requests.

1 I'd like a room for tonight.
2 I'd like the code for the car park.
3 We'd like a different room.
4 We'd like dinner at eight o'clock.

5 Listen and respond requests

🔊 **110** Listen to the hotel receptionist. Respond with the words.

1

> Good afternoon. Can I help you?

> Yes, I'd like a taxi, please.

1 a taxi
2 the key for my room
3 a room for two nights
4 breakfast in my room

9e A great place for a weekend

Writing travel advice

1 Writing skill *because*

a Write *because* in the correct place in the sentences.

              because

1   Book your tickets online↑it's quick and easy.

2   You can swim every day the beach is next to the hotel.

3   Stay in bed and breakfasts they're cheap and friendly.

4   Don't go in winter it's very cold.

5   There are a lot of hotels it's a popular place.

6   Don't take a bus they aren't comfortable.

b Match the parts of the sentences.

1   Acapulco is a great place for a weekend because

2   It's easy to travel around because

3   Don't go in August because

4   Go from October to March because

5   Don't miss the cliff divers because

a   it's very rainy.

b   the weather is dry and sunny.

c   there are a lot of taxis and buses.

d   there is a lot to see and do!

e   they are amazing!

2 Read the article about Acapulco. Complete the article with this information.

a   American students

b   it's a 45-minute flight from Mexico City

c   play golf next to the sea

d   water parks for all the family

3 Read the information about Legoland. Write a paragraph for parents.

Legoland

- great place / families
- near London
- a lot of attractions
- August / a lot of people
- a hotel in the park
- the children's train / great for young children

Acapulco

Acapulco is a great place for a weekend because there is a lot to see and do! There's an international airport and [1] _____ . It's easy to travel around because there are a lot of taxis and buses. Acapulco has a wet season. Don't go in August because it's very rainy. Go from October to March because the weather is dry and sunny.

You can go fishing in Acapulco Bay and [2] _____ . There are theme parks and [3] _____ . In spring, it's a popular place with [4] _____ – don't go in April because there are a lot of students at that time. Finally, don't miss the cliff divers because they are amazing!

A cliff diver in Acapulco

Learning skills recording verbs

There are some common verb + noun combinations:

take a bag

take a bus

When you write new verbs in your notebook, write these combinations.

1 Add these words to the diagrams and make expressions with *take*, *book* and *travel*.

a hotel	a photo	a suitcase
by bus	online	to Africa

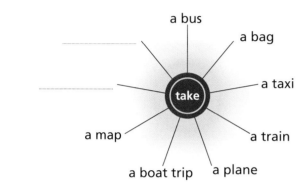

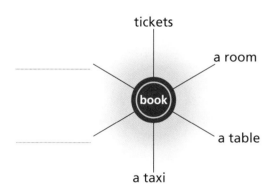

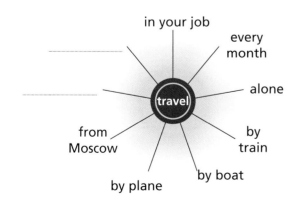

2 Make your own diagrams for the verbs *go* and *have* in your vocabulary notebook.

Check!

3 What can you remember? The answers to the questions are in Student's Book Unit 9 and Workbook Unit 9.

1 Which country is Machu Picchu in?

2 Where's the city of Novosibirsk?

3 How long is Lake Baikal?

4 What's the name of the railway from Moscow to Vladivostok?

5 Where can you listen to Fado?

6 What's Chichen Itza?

7 What's the capital of New Zealand?

8 Is there an airport in Acapulco?

4 Complete the word puzzle. The sentences are about a hotel room.

1 There are some flowers on the _____ . (five letters)

2 There are two _____ in the room. (four letters)

3 Is there any mineral water in the _____ ? (six letters)

4 We can sit on the _____ to watch TV. (four letters)

5 There's a shower, but there isn't a _____ . (four letters)

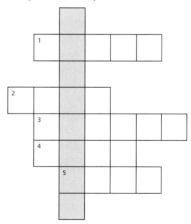

5 Complete the word in the shaded squares.

Unit 10 Famous people

10a People in history

Vocabulary years

1 🎵 **111** Listen and write the years.

1 _____ 2012 _____
2 _____
3 _____
4 _____
5 _____
6 _____

2 🎵 **112** Listen and write the years in words.

1 _____ nineteen ninety-eight _____
2 _____
3 _____
4 _____
5 _____
6 _____

Vocabulary dates

3 🎵 **113** Listen and complete the dates.

1 _____ 1st _____ January
2 _____ July
3 _____ August
4 _____ May
5 _____ February
6 _____ December

4 🎵 **113** Listen again and repeat the dates from Exercise 3.

5 Write the ordinal numbers in words.

a 1st _____ first _____
b 2nd _____
c 3rd _____
d 4th _____
e 5th _____
f 10th _____
g 11th _____
h 12th _____
i 13th _____
j 21st _____

Reading a scientist

6 Look at the photo. Read about this scientist and complete the notes.

name: ¹_____
job: ²_____ and first ³_____
born: on ⁴_____ in ⁵_____
husband's nationality: ⁶_____
husband's job: ⁷_____
children born: in ⁸_____

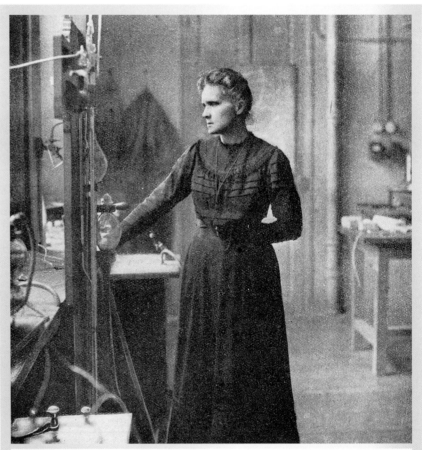

Marie Skłodowska Curie was born on 7th November 1867. She was a scientist. She was the first woman winner of a Nobel Prize and the first woman professor at the University of Paris. Marie was born in Poland. Her husband, Pierre, was French. He was a scientist too. Their two children, Irene and Eve, were born in France.

Grammar *be*: *was/were*

7 Read about Alfred Nobel and complete the article with these words.

> brothers   engineer   October   parents
> rich   scientist   Sweden

Alfred Nobel was born on 21st ¹ _____ 1833. He was a ² _____ . He was the inventor of dynamite. Nobel was born in ³ _____ . His ⁴ _____ were Immanuel – an ⁵ _____ – and Andriette. Nobel's ⁶ _____ , Ludvig and Robert, were very ⁷ _____ . They were in the oil industry on the Caspian Sea.

8 Complete the sentences with *was* and *were*.

1 Sally Ride _____ an astronaut on the Space Shuttle.
2 Christopher Columbus and Vasco da Gama _____ explorers in the 15th century.
3 Alfred Nobel _____ born in Sweden in 1833.
4 Five members of Marie Curie's family _____ winners of Nobel Prizes.
5 Mao Zedong _____ born in China in 1893.
6 Mao Zedong's father _____ a farmer.

9 🔾 **114** Look at the information about John Logie Baird. Write sentences with *was* and *were*. Listen and check.

1 *John Logie Baird was born in 1888.*
2 _____
3 _____
4 _____
5 _____
6 _____

John Logie Baird

- 1888
- an engineer and inventor
- the inventor of television
- parents from Scotland
- born in Scotland
- children born in England

10 Pronunciation *was/were* weak forms

🔾 **114** Listen again and repeat the sentences from Exercise 9.

11 Dictation years and dates: *in* and *on*

a 🔾 **115** Listen and complete the sentences.

1 Irene Curie _____ .
2 Eve Curie _____ .
3 John Logie Baird _____ .
4 Sally Ride _____ .
5 Alfred Nobel _____ .
6 Mao Zedong _____ .

b Choose the correct option.

1 We use *in* with *dates / years*.
2 We use *on* with *dates / years*.

12 Grammar extra *there was/were*

THERE WAS/WERE	
present	**past**
There's a problem with the television.	There **was** a problem with the television.
There are two children in the family.	There **were** two children in the family.

a Look at the grammar box. What is the past of *there is* and *there are*?

b Complete the sentences with *was* or *were*.

1 There _____ an accident on the Space Shuttle in 1986.
2 There _____ 135 Space Shuttle flights from 1981 to 2011.
3 There _____ eight children in Alfred Nobel's family.
4 There _____ five Nobel prize winners in Marie Curie's family.
5 There _____ 415 million people in China in 1893.
6 There _____ a revolution in China in 1949.

John Logie Baird

10b My history

Vocabulary describing people

1 Look at the pictures. Choose the correct option.

1 People in a lot of countries know him. He's very *famous / clever*.
2 I like his stories about his past. He's very *interesting / popular*.
3 He's a *funny / good* actor – he has two Oscars.
4 She's a *happy / great* cook. I love her food.
5 I like my classmates. They're really *famous / funny*.

2 Vocabulary extra adjectives

Complete the sentences with these words.

bad	boring	terrible	unhappy

1 He isn't interesting – he's _____ .
2 She isn't a great singer – she's _____ .
3 He isn't a good actor – he's a _____ actor.
4 He isn't happy – he's _____ .

Reading my history

3 Read about Martin Freeman. Are the sentences true (T) or false (F)?

1 He was Sherlock Holmes in the *Sherlock* TV series.
2 He was born in 1971.
3 His parents were famous actors.
4 He was ill when he was a child.
5 He was good at sports.
6 He was in his first film when he was twenty-three.

Radio 6   19.30   April

My history

This week: Martin Freeman

Martin Freeman is an actor in films and on TV. His roles include Dr Watson in *Sherlock* and Bilbo Baggins in *The Hobbit* films. He was also in the TV series *Fargo*. Martin was born in 1971. There were five children in his family. His parents weren't actors. When Martin was a child, he was often ill. At school, he wasn't good at sports, but he was good at acting. He was a student in London and he was in his first film in 1997.

Glossary
ill (adjective) /ɪl/

a **role** (noun) /rəʊl/ a part an actor has in a film

Grammar *be*: *was/were* negative and question forms

4 Rewrite the sentences about Martin Freeman with the word in brackets and *wasn't* or *weren't*.

1 He was born in England. (New Zealand)
   He wasn't born in New Zealand.

2 His parents were poor. (rich)

3 His first job was in a TV show. (film)

4 His first film roles were small. (big)

5 He was an unhappy child. (happy)

5 Write true sentences for you.

1 I / born / 1971
   I wasn't born in 1971.

2 parents / actors

3 grandparents / famous

4 my brother / a student in London

5 I / in a TV show in 1997

6 🔘 **116** Put the words in order to make questions for an actress. Listen and check.

1 big / your / was / school / ?

2 science / you / good at / were / ?

3 teachers / were / friendly / the / ?

4 the / interesting / lessons / were / ?

5 best friend / your / in your class / was / ?

6 nice / were / classmates / your / ?

7 🔘 **116** Listen again. Then write *yes* and *no* answers.

1 *No, it wasn't.*
2
3
4
5
6

8 Pronunciation extra *was* and *were* strong forms

🔘 **117** Listen and repeat the questions and answers from Exercises 6 and 7.

9 Listen and respond your school days

🔘 **118** Listen to six questions. Respond with your own words.

1

Was your school big?

Yes, it was.

No, it wasn't.

© New Line Cinema/The Kobal Collection

10c An Aztec leader

Listening an Aztec leader

1 🔊 **119** Look at the picture and listen to the radio programme about historical documents. Answer the questions.

1 Who was this man?

2 Where was he from?

3 What was his name?

2 🔊 **119** Listen again. Are the sentences true (T) or false (F)?

1 He lived in South America.

2 Moctezuma was born in about 1466.

3 He died in 1520.

4 He was the ruler of the Aztec empire from 1502 to 1520.

Grammar regular past simple verbs

3 Complete the sentences with *was born, lived* and *died.*

1 The Maya people _____ in Central America.

2 David Bowie _____ in 2016.

3 Mother Teresa _____ in Albania and India.

4 Adele _____ in 1988.

5 Ayrton Senna _____ in a racing accident.

6 Nicole Kidman _____ in Hawaii, but she _____ in Australia.

4 Grammar extra *was / were* with question words

WAS / WERE WITH QUESTION WORDS				
	Was Were	I/he/she/it you/we/they	from	Peru?
Where	was were	I/he/she/it you/we/they	from?	

a Look at the grammar box. Then put the words in order to make questions. Underline the question word.

1 your parents / where / from / were / ?

2 was / born / when / your father / ?

3 your grandmother's name / was / what / ?

4 at school / was / who / your best friend / ?

b Write your own answers to the questions in Exercise 1a.

1 _____

2 _____

3 _____

4 _____

5 Word focus extra *first* and *last*

Complete the sentences with *first* or *last*.

1 The _____ man in space was Yuri Gagarin.

2 The _____ day of April is the 30th.

3 Was the _____ of January a Monday this year?

4 What was Magellan's _____ name?

5 What time is the _____ bus at night?

6 I was 25 on my _____ birthday.

7 The _____ American expedition to Everest was in 1963.

8 Were you at home _____ night?

10d I'm sorry

Vocabulary activities

1 🔘 **120** Listen and match the conversations (1–6) with the pictures (a–f).

a

b

c

d

e

f

2 🔘 **120** Listen again. Look at the people in the pictures in Exercise 1. Write their words.

a *I was asleep.*
b
c
d
e
f

Real life apologizing

3 🔘 **121** Complete the conversations with these sentences. Listen and check.

a Don't worry.   e I'm sorry I'm late.
b I was at home.   f I was busy at work.
c I'm very sorry.   g That's OK.
d I wasn't well.

1 A student (S) and a teacher (T) at a college
   T: Hi. Where were you this morning?
   S: I'm sorry. ¹_____
   T: OK, but why were you at home?
   S: ²_____
   T: Oh dear!
   S: ³_____
       I'm OK now, thanks.

2 Two colleagues at work
   P: Hello!
   C: Hi, Paul. ⁴_____
       There was a traffic jam.
   P: ⁵_____ Don't worry.
       I was late too.

3 Two friends in a café
   F: Hello, Jake.
   J: Hi! Where were you last night?
   F: Oh, ⁶_____
   J: We were all at the restaurant.
   F: ⁷_____ There were
       a lot of phone calls.
   J: OK.

4 Pronunciation sentence stress

🔘 **122** Listen and repeat six sentences.

5 Listen and respond apologizing

🔘 **123** Listen to the questions. Respond with the words.

1
   Where were you last night?

   I'm really sorry. I was at home.

1 at home   4 busy at work
2 not well   5 bus / late
3 a traffic jam   6 asleep

10e Sorry!

Writing an email

1 Read four emails from David. Are they apologies (A) or expressions of sympathy (S)?

1 ....
2 ....
3 ....
4 ....

1

> ¹ .... Jack
>
> Sorry about yesterday! My phone was at home! Here's the website: www.bookbook.org
>
> ² ....
>
> David

2

> ³ .... Ms Robson
>
> I apologize for the problem with our website information. Please visit our website again to see the correct information.
>
> ⁴ ....
>
> David Marr

3

> ⁵ .... Amanda
>
> I'm so sorry things are difficult for you at the moment. I hope to see you at work soon.
>
> ⁶ ....
>
> David Marr

4

> ⁷ .... Angelica
>
> I'm very sorry, but I can't come to class this week. I'm really busy at work. See you next week.
>
> ⁸ ....
>
> David

3 Match the information 1–4 with a–d from four emails.

1 don't know your new phone number
2 can't come to conference in June
3 the delay in my reply to your email
4 you aren't well

a busy time in the office
b here is the information
c hope to see you soon
d send it

4 Write four emails using the information in Exercise 3 and these names. Use expressions from Exercise 2. Express apologies or sympathy.

1 Ali / Jim
2 Ms Brown / Sandra Cross
3 Mr Panjabi / Luisa Torres
4 Gina / Tomas

2 Writing skill expressions in emails

Complete the emails with these expressions. More than one expression is possible.

All the best
Best wishes
Dear
Hi
Love,
Best regards

Learning skills standard expressions

There are a lot of situations where you can use standard expressions. Learn these expressions and the standard responses.

1 When can you use these expressions (1–10)? Match them with the situations (a–j).

1 'I'm sorry.'
  'That's OK.'

2 'Nice to meet you.'
  'Nice to meet you too.'

3 'Thank you very much.'
  'You're welcome.'

4 'Excuse me. Where's the bank?'

5 'Can I help you?'
  'Can I have a coffee, please?'

6 'How much is this?'
  'How much are these?'
  'Can I pay with a card?'
  'Here you are.'

7 'Let's go to the cinema tonight.'
  'That's a good idea.'

8 'What's the matter?'
  'I'm thirsty.'
  'Why don't you have a cup of coffee?'

9 'Can I speak to Jack, please?'
  'One moment, please.'

10 'I'd like a taxi, please.'
  'I'd like to book a table.'
  'Certainly.'

a You meet a person for the first time.
b You receive a present.
c You request something.
d You want to apologize.
e You want to have something to drink.
f You want to buy something.
g You're in the street on holiday.
h You're on the telephone.
i You want to go out for the evening.
j There's a problem.

2 Write the equivalent expressions in your own language in your vocabulary notebook.

3 Think of three everyday situations. What do people say? Can you say it in English? Write the conversations.

1 ....
  ....
  ....

2 ....
  ....
  ....

3 ....
  ....
  ....

Check!

4 Complete the word puzzle.

1 Geronimo was a leader of the
   .... people. (six letters)
2 Where were Yuri Gagarin and Valentina Tereshkova from? (six letters)
3 What nationality was the first woman at the top of Everest? (eight letters)
4 Where was Ferdinand Magellan born? (eight letters)
5 The Inca Empire was in .... America. (five letters)
6 Where was Roald Amundsen from? (six letters)
7 What was the name of the people from Central America? (four letters)

1						
2						
3						
4						
5						
6						
7						

5 What is the word in the shaded squares? Write it here. ....

Unit 11 True stories

11a A surprise in the restaurant

Grammar irregular past simple verbs

1 Look at the pictures and read the sentences. Put the sentences in order (1–8).

a   We had a salad for the first course. ....

b   My wife called the waiter. ....

c   It was our wedding anniversary on 5th
November.   *1*

d   I finished my salad. ....

e   We went to a nice restaurant for dinner. ....

f   I found a snail on the plate. ....

g   He was very sorry. ....

h   We took a taxi to town. ....

2 Look at the story again. Complete the verbs from the story. Are they regular (R) or irregular (I) past simple forms?

1 h *ad*   *I*

2 fi

3 w

4 fo

5 c

6 t

3 Dictation a surprise in the restaurant

🎧 **124** Listen and write four sentences about the story in Exercise 1. Who is the speaker? Is he the taxi driver or the waiter?

1 ....

2 ....

3 ....

4 ....

Grammar extra regular past simple verbs

4 Write the past simple form of these verbs.

1 call

2 die

3 discover

4 finish

5 kill

6 live

7 start

8 study

9 walk

5 Complete the sentences with the past simple form of six verbs from Exercise 4.

1 When I was young, we .... in a small house.

2 When I was five years old, I .... school.

3 My grandfather .... at the age of ninety-one.

4 We .... history and science at school.

5 I .... to my English class yesterday.

6 We .... Unit 10 last week.

6 Pronunciation *-ed* regular past simple verbs

🎧 **125** Listen and repeat the sentences from Exercise 5.

7 Complete the article about an archaeological discovery with the correct form of these verbs.

be   be   die   discover   find   have   live   study

In 2002, archaeologists [1] .... an interesting body of a man. They [2] .... at Stonehenge, in the south of England. The archaeologists think he [3] .... a rich man – he [4] .... tools and arrows with him. He [5] .... about 4,000 years ago – the archaeologists [6] .... the body. They [7] .... that the man [8] .... in the Alps in Switzerland. Why was he in England? It's a mystery.

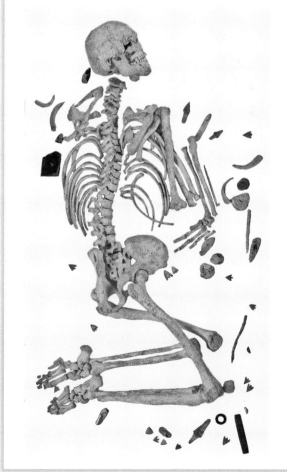

11b Life stories

Reading Michael Palin

1 Read the article about Michael Palin. Answer the questions.

1 Where did he go to university?

....

2 What jobs did he do after university?

....

3 When did he make his first travel programme?

....

4 When did he start his diary?

....

5 How many years of his life are in the diaries?

....

2 Read the article again and find the past simple form of these verbs.

1 study   *studied*
2 meet
3 make
4 find
5 change
6 go
7 write
8 follow
9 start
10 publish
11 prepare
12 remember

Michael Palin: writer, actor, TV presenter

Michael Palin was born in 1943. He studied history at Oxford University. Palin met his wife in 1959, but they didn't marry until 1966. After university, he didn't work as a historian – he was an actor and a TV writer from 1965 to 1980. He was a member of *Monty Python*. Then in 1980 he made a TV show about a trip by train and he found that he loved travel and exploration. So he changed his job. In 1988, he went 'Around the world in 80 days'. Jules Verne wrote the story in 1873. Palin followed the same route. He made travel programmes for thirty years.

Palin started to write a personal diary in 1969. He wrote something almost every day. In 2006, he published three books of his diaries. Each book was about a period of ten years in his life. Palin says when he prepared the three books, he remembered many things from his life.

Grammar past simple negative and question forms

3 Read the sentences and look at the word in brackets. Write two true sentences.

1 Michael Palin studied French at university. (history)

Michael Palin didn't study French at university.
He studied history at university.

2 He made a film in 1980. (TV show)

3 He wrote *Around the world in 80 days.* (Jules Verne)

4 He travelled to the South Pole in 1999. (1991)

5 He went around the Pacific Ocean in two months. (ten months)

6 He walked across the Sahara Desert in 2005. (2002)

4 You are an interviewer. Write questions for Michael Palin.

1 write your diary / at university?
Did you write your diary at university?

2 your wife / go / on your trips?

3 drive / to the South Pole?

4 meet / interesting people?

5 your children / read / your diaries?

6 write a book / last year?

5 Pronunciation *did you … ?*

a 126 Listen and check your questions from Exercise 4.

b 126 Listen again and repeat the questions.

6 Complete Michael Palin's answers to the questions.

1 No, *I didn't* .
2 No, .
3 No, .
4 Yes, .
5 Yes, .
6 Yes, .

Vocabulary life events

7 Complete the sentences with these verbs in the correct form. Then choose the name of the person in sentence 8.

be go leave live meet start study

1 She ___ born in 1964.
2 She ___ with her brother and her parents.
3 She ___ to school in Chicago.
4 She ___ school in 1981.
5 She ___ at Harvard University.
6 She ___ work in a law firm in Chicago.
7 She ___ her husband at work.
8 Her name is *Angela Merkel / Michelle Obama / Chelsea Clinton.*

8 Listen and respond life events

127 Listen to six questions. Respond with your own words. Give extra information.

1 *When were you born?*

I was born in 1995.

11c A problem in the Arctic

Reading and listening a trip to the North Pole

1 Read the article and answer the questions.

1 Who was on the expedition?

....

2 Where did they go?

....

3 What did they carry their equipment on?

....

4 What did they see on the first day?

....

Arctic trek

In 2006, Borge Ousland, from Norway, was on an expedition to the North Pole. He was with a South African, Mike Horn. They travelled across the ice on skis. They had sledges with their equipment. On the first day, they saw a polar bear. That night, it ate part of their rubber boat. One day, the weather was really bad. Listen to their story.

Glossary

equipment (noun) /ɪˈkwɪpmənt/

a rubber boat (noun) /ˌrʌbə ˈbəʊt/

a polar bear (noun) /ˌpəʊlə ˈbeə/

skis (noun) /skiːs/

2 🔊 **128** Listen to the story. Put the sentences in order (1–6).

a Borge Ousland helped him.

b It was snowy and windy.   *1*

c Mike Horn fell into the sea.

d Ousland started a fire.

e The ice broke.

f They dried Horn's clothes.

Grammar past simple Wh- questions

3 Put the words in order to make questions about the Arctic trek story.

1 Borge Ousland / did / who / travel with / ?

....

2 go / did / when / to the North Pole / they / ?

....

3 the polar bear / did / eat / what / ?

....

4 did / fall / Mike Horn / where / ?

....

5 Mike Horn / fall / why / did / ?

....

6 start a fire / Borge Ousland / did / why / ?

....

4 What is the answer to the questions in Exercise 3? Choose the correct option.

1 Mike Horn / skis

2 in 2006 / in 2010

3 their sledges / their boat

4 onto the ice / into the sea

5 because the ice broke / because his skis broke

6 to make some food / to dry Horn's clothes

5 Word focus get

Complete the sentences with these words.

bread	bus	email	home	presents
the North Pole				

1 Did they get to .... in the end?

2 Did you get my .... ? I sent it yesterday.

3 I didn't get any .... The shop wasn't open.

4 She got some great .... for her birthday.

5 We can get a .... to the station.

6 The train was late, so we didn't get .... until midnight.

11d Did you have a good time?

Real life talking about the past

1 💿 **129** Put the conversations in order. Listen and check.

1 a Did you have a nice meal on Saturday?   *1*
  b I found a snail in my food!
  c No, we didn't.
  d Oh dear! What did you do?
  e Oh? Why not?
  f We left the restaurant and we didn't pay!

2 a Did you go scuba diving?
  b Did you have a nice holiday?
  c We went to the Red Sea. It was beautiful.
  d Where did you go?
  e Yes, thanks, we did.
  f Well, we didn't go scuba diving, but we went swimming.

3 a Nothing. I didn't have my laptop with me.
  b Did you have a good trip last week?
  c Oh? Why not?
  d Six hours! What did you do?
  e The weather was really bad. I was at the airport for six hours.
  f No, I didn't.

2 Pronunciation *didn't*

💿 **130** Listen and repeat these sentences with *didn't*.

1 We didn't pay.
2 We didn't go scuba diving.
3 I didn't have my laptop with me.
4 I didn't have a good trip.

3 Vocabulary time expressions

Today is Thursday. Put the time expressions in order.

a last month
b last night   *1*
c last week
d last weekend
e last year
f on Tuesday
g three days ago
h yesterday morning

4 Listen and respond talking about the past

💿 **131** Listen to six questions. Respond with your own words.

1   *Did you have a good weekend?*

      Yes, thanks, I did.   *No, I didn't.*

11e Childhood memories

Writing a life story

1 Think of a time in your childhood, for example when you were ten years old. Answer the questions with full sentences.

1 Who was your best friend?
   My best friend was Denise Lagarde.

2 What were your hobbies?

3 What was your favourite food?

4 What was your favourite TV show? Why?

5 What were your parents' jobs?

6 Where did you live?

7 Who did you live with?

8 Who were your neighbours?

9 Where did you go to school?

10 What subjects did you like at school?

11 Who was your favourite teacher? Why?

12 Were you a member of any clubs?

2 Writing skill *when*

Write five sentences with the pairs of sentences. Start with *when*. Don't forget the comma.

1 I was five. My brother was born.

2 I was at school. I learned a lot of English.

3 I was at secondary school. I played football and basketball.

4 My parents were children. They lived in Mexico.

5 I was a child. My favourite food was pizza.

3 Choose one of these writing tasks. Use *when* in some of your sentences.

a Use your answers from Exercise 1 to write a paragraph about your childhood.

b Imagine you are one of the people in this photo. Use the questions in Exercise 1 to help you write a paragraph about your childhood.

Learning skills irregular verbs

1 Complete the list of irregular past simple verbs. The missing past simple forms are all in Student's Book Unit 11.

Present	Past simple	Translation
break	broke	
buy	bought	
choose	chose	
come	came	
cut		
do		
draw	drew	
drink	drank	
drive	drove	
eat		
fall		
feel	felt	
find	found	
fly	flew	
forget	forgot	
get		
give	gave	
go		
grow	grew	
have		
hear	heard	
hide		
hurt	hurt	

2 Choose six verbs from the list and write sentences or expressions in your vocabulary notebook.

Present	Past simple	Translation
know		
leave		
make	made	
meet		
pay	paid	
put	put	
read	read /red/	
ride	rode	
run	ran	
say	said	
see		
sing		
sleep	slept	
speak	spoke	
swim	swam	
take		
tell	told	
think	thought	
throw		
understand	understood	
wake	woke	
wear	wore	
write	wrote	

Check!

3 What can you remember? The answers to the questions are in Student's Book Unit 11 and Workbook Unit 11.

1 What was the Iceman's name?

....

2 Where is the museum the Iceman is in? (the name of the country)

....

3 What did the Iceman have with him?
Arrows, a bag and a ....

4 Which city is famous for Mardi Gras?

....

5 Where is the *tsingy*?

....

6 Why are the rocks in the *tsingy* dangerous?
Because they are ....

7 What is a lemur?
A kind of ....

8 Who was the writer of *Around the world in 80 days*?

....

9 Which desert did Michael Palin go across in 2002?

....

10 Name an animal that lives in the Arctic.

....

12a At home

Vocabulary rooms in a house

1 Look at the picture. Write the rooms.

1 a o o b h m r t

....

2 e o o b d m r

....

3 e i c h k n t

....

4 i i o o d g m n n r

....

....

5 i i o o g l m n r v

....

....

2 Where do you do these things?

1 watch TV
I watch TV in the living room.

2 eat lunch

....

....

3 cook

....

....

4 sleep

....

....

5 have a bath

....

....

Grammar present continuous

3 Look at the photo and read the caption. Answer the questions.

1 Where are the people from?

....

2 Where are they?

....

3 How many people are in the room?

....

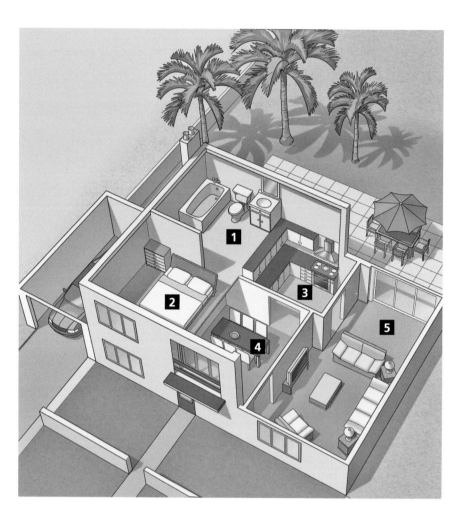

This is a family at home in Kolkata, India. The six children are in the living room of their grandfather's house. Their mother is giving a cup of tea to her daughter. The cup of tea is for the grandfather.

4 🔊 **132** Write sentences about the people. Listen and check.

1 the man / sit / on a chair

2 the children / sit / on the floor

3 the boy / look / at the camera

4 the girl / stand / near a small table

   she / wear / a dress

5 Pronunciation extra -ing

🔊 **132** Listen again and repeat the sentences from Exercise 4.

6 Write questions and answers about the people in the photo.

1 the man / wear jeans?
   Q: *Is the man wearing jeans?*
   A: *No, he isn't.*

2 the children / watch TV?
   Q:
   A:

3 the man / read a book?
   Q:
   A:

4 the children / sit?
   Q:
   A:

5 the girl / make tea?
   Q:
   A:

6 the boys / wear shorts?
   Q:
   A:

7 Rewrite the sentences in the form given in brackets

1 They're making lunch. (question)

2 He's reading the newspaper. (negative)

3 Are you watching TV? (affirmative)

4 We aren't washing the car. (affirmative)

5 You aren't eating. (question)

6 Is she sitting on the floor? (negative)

Listening at home

8 🔊 **133** Complete the sentences in a telephone conversation. Listen and check.

JOE: *Hi Ali.* ¹ What / you / do?

ALI: *Nothing special.* ² I / watch / TV.

JOE: ³ What / you / watch?

ALI: *It's a programme about shopping.*
JOE: *OK.*
ALI: ⁴ you / watch / TV?

JOE: ⁵ No, I / not.

      Jack is here. ⁶ We / play / a video game.

ALI: *Oh! Is it good?*
JOE: *Yes, it is.*
ALI: *Wait for me.* ⁷ I / come / to your house.

JOE: *Now?*
ALI: *Yes.* ⁸ I / leave / the house right now.

JOE: *OK, great. See you soon.*

9 Listen and respond at home

🔊 **134** Listen to five questions about what you are doing now. Respond with your own words.

1   *Are you in the living room?*   *No, I'm not. I'm in the kitchen.*

12b Next weekend

Vocabulary weekend activities

1 Write the correct verb with each noun. Use one verb more than once.

cook	get up	go	go out	have
make	meet	play	read	visit

1 .... a party
2 .... family
3 .... football
4 .... for a meal
5 .... for a walk
6 .... friends
7 .... late
8 .... shopping
9 .... the newspaper
10 .... to a concert
11 .... a cake
12 .... the newspaper

2 Look at the pictures and write sentences with these words and nouns from Exercise 1.

go	go out	meet	play	read
visit				

1 Tibor / with his friends
Tibor is playing football with his friends.

2 Adela and Naomi / on Saturday evening

3 Mike / this weekend

4 Rowan / the newspaper

5 Leila / with colleagues / tomorrow

6 Joe and Sue / with their children / on Saturday morning

Grammar present continuous for the future

3 Look at the sentences in Exercise 2. Are the people doing the activities now or at a time in the future? Write *now* or the future time expression from the sentence.

1 _____ *now* _____
2 _____
3 _____
4 _____
5 _____
6 _____

4 🔊 **135** Listen to Rosa and Carla's conversation, and complete their diaries. Today is Thursday.

Rosa's diary

Thursday	–
Friday morning evening	– 1 _____
Saturday morning evening	2 _____ 3 _____
Sunday	4 _____
Monday morning evening	– 5 _____

Carla's diary

Thursday	–
Friday morning evening	– going to the cinema
Saturday	6 _____
Sunday morning evening	7 _____ lunch with sister –
Monday	–

5 🔊 **135** Listen again and complete the questions with time expressions.

1 Are you coming to the cinema
_____ ?
2 Are you leaving _____ ?
3 Is she getting married
_____ ?
4 Are you coming back from Edinburgh
_____ ?

6 Write sentences with the information you completed (1–7) in the diaries.

1 *Rosa is working on Friday evening.*
2 _____
3 _____
4 _____
5 _____
6 _____
7 _____

7 Dictation the weekend

a 🔊 **136** Listen and write the questions about weekend activities.

1 _____
2 _____
3 _____
4 _____

b Write your own answers to the questions in Exercise 7a.

1 _____
2 _____
3 _____
4 _____

8 Pronunciation *going* and *doing*

🔊 **136** Listen again and repeat the questions from Exercise 7a.

12c A different kind of weekend

Listening weekend courses

1 🔊 **137** Listen to two people talk about their weekends. Match the speaker with the photo (a or b).

Speaker 1 ....

Speaker 2 ....

2 🔊 **137** Listen again. Answer the questions for each speaker.

1   Where does he/she go at the weekend?

    ....

2   Does he/she go with friends or alone?

    ....

3   What did he/she do last weekend?

    ....

4   What is he/she doing next weekend?

    ....

Grammar prepositions of place (2)

3 Read the sentences about a house. Choose the correct option.

1   The garden is *behind* / *under* the house.
2   There's a small table *on* / *under* the window.
3   There's a lamp *between* / *on* the desk in the living room.
4   The kitchen is *behind* / *between* the living room and the bathroom.

Grammar tense review

4 Complete the sentences with the correct form of the verbs.

1   She .... (work) in an office in London.
2   She .... (meet) her friends tomorrow.
3   He .... (go) on a course last month.
4   I .... (read) the newspaper yesterday.
5   We .... (go) climbing this weekend.
6   He sometimes .... (go) out with his friends.

5 Word focus extra *do*

a Look at the questions and answers. Write questions with the correct form of *do*.

1   'What / you / do?'

    ....

    'I'm a police officer.'

2   'What / you / do?'

    ....

    'I'm reading the newspaper.'

3   'What / you / usually / do / at the weekend?'

    ....

    'I go cycling.'

4   'What / you / do / last weekend?'

    ....

    'I did a painting course.'

5   'What / you / do / this weekend?'

    ....

    'I'm going to a festival.'

b Write your own answers to the questions in Exercise 5a.

1   ....
2   ....
3   ....
4   ....
5   ....

12d Would you like to come?

Vocabulary times and places

1 Complete the sentences with these words.

> at   at   in   in   next   on   on
> tomorrow

1   We're moving house _____ month.
2   I go to my English class _____ the afternoon.
3   We had lunch _____ their house last week.
4   Let's meet _____ evening.
5   My brother lives _____ Greece.
6   I'm starting a new job _____ Monday morning.
7   We usually get up _____ half past seven.
8   Dinner is _____ the table.

Real life offers and invitations

2 🎵 **138** Complete the conversations with these expressions. You can use some expressions more than once. Then listen and check.

> do you   I can't   I'd   would you

1   A: Hi, Belinda. Come in.
    B: Hi. How are you?
    A: I'm fine. [1] _____ like a drink? Tea or coffee?
    B: Yes, tea's great. Thanks.
    A: OK, just a moment.

2   C: [2] _____ want to go to the cinema this week?
    D: Erm, which day?
    C: Friday evening?
    D: Sorry, [3] _____ make it on Friday.
    C: OK. [4] _____ want to go on Thursday?
    D: Yes, that's fine.

3   E: What are you doing this weekend?
    F: We're going to the mountains.
    E: Oh, [5] _____ like to come.
    F: Great! [6] _____ like to come in our car?
    E: Yes, please.

3 Pronunciation *would you … ?*

🎵 **139** Listen and repeat these questions.

1   Would you like a cup of coffee?
2   Would you like to come with us on Sunday?
3   Would you like a sandwich?
4   Would you like to go for a walk tomorrow?
5   Would you like to meet one day next week?
6   Would you like a drink?

4 Listen and respond *would you like … ?*

🎵 **139** Listen to the questions from Exercise 3 again. Respond in the negative with your own words.

1

> *Would you like a cup of coffee?*

> *No, thanks. I don't drink coffee.*

12e Thank you!

Writing a thank you note

1 Read the thank you note. Complete the sentences with *Dani* and *Francesca*.

1 .... went to visit ....

2 .... sent some photos to ....

> Dear Dani
>
> Thank you very much for the photos. They're great! I'm putting them on my computer now. It was lovely to see you at the weekend. Your new house is beautiful. Are you coming to see us soon?
>
> Love
>
> Francesca

2 Writing skill spelling: verb endings

a Read the note again. <u>Underline</u> these verbs in the note. Write the infinitives. What's the spelling change?

1 putting ....

2 coming ....

b Match the spelling rules (1–4) for the present continuous with the verbs (a–d).

1 Add *-ing*.

2 Make the last letter double and add *-ing*.

3 Change *ie* to *y* and add *-ing*.

4 Take off *e* and add *-ing*.

a arrive → arriving

b fly → flying

c get → getting

d lie → lying

c Complete the table. Make sure you spell the verbs correctly. Use a dictionary if necessary.

	Present continuous	Present simple (*he/she/it*)	Past simple
arrive			
come			
do			
drive			
fly			
get			
have			

	Present continuous	Present simple (*he/she/it*)	Past simple
leave			
lie			
make			
move			
phone			
run			
see			
sit			
smile			
study			
swim			
travel			
work			

3 Match the situations (1–4) with the comments (a–h).

1 You stayed at your friend's house.

2 You went to a meal at your friend's house.

3 Your friend took you to hospital.

4 Your friend sent you some DVDs.

a I had a great time.

b I watched the first one last night.

c I'm fine now.

d It was delicious.

e It was great to see you.

f It was very kind of you.

g They were really interesting.

h You're a fantastic cook!

4 Write a 'thank you' note to a friend. Choose one of the situations in Exercise 3.

> Dear ....
>
> ....
>
> ....
>
> ....
>
> Thanks again. Speak to you soon.
>
> Love,
>
> ....

5 Check the spelling in your note.

Learning skills assess your progress

1 Look at part 4 in the progress questionnaire on page 67.
What did you focus on in Units 9–12?

My progress in English: Units 9–12

1 **Tick (✓) the option that is true for you.**
My progress in Units 9–12 is:
Excellent ☐   Good ☐   OK ☐   Not very good ☐

---

2 Complete the questionnaire for *Life* Beginner.

Read the sentences. What can you do in English?			
Mark the option that is true for you.	I'm good at this. (✓)	I'm not sure about this. (?)	I'm not very good at this. (✗)
I can talk about people.			
I can talk about families.			
I can describe places.			
I can talk about abilities.			
I can discuss likes and dislikes.			
I can talk about people's lives.			
I can talk about travel.			
I can talk about the past.			
I can talk about things that are happening now.			
I can talk about the future.			
I can give personal information.			
I can use expressions on special occasions.			
I can ask about and say the time.			
I can buy snacks.			
I can buy things in shops.			
I can give opinions.			
I can ask about problems.			
I can make suggestions.			
I can make phone calls.			
I can make requests.			
I can apologize.			
I can complete a form.			
I can write greetings cards.			
I can write a postcard.			
I can write an email.			
I can write an invitation.			

Check!

3 Use the picture clues to complete the sentences. The words are in Student's Book Unit 12.

1 I'm reading the _____ .
2 He's _____ his clothes.
3 She's looking out of the _____ .
4 This man's a _____ .
5 He's buying a new _____ .

🎵 140

LISTENING TEST

SECTION 1

Questions 1 and 2

Choose the correct letter (A, B or C).

Example:

What day do the English lessons start?
A Monday
Ⓑ Tuesday
C Wednesday

---

1 Which room is the English test in?
   A Room 14
   B Room 15
   C Room 16

2 How long does the English test last?
   A 1 hour 10 minutes
   B 1 hour 20 minutes
   C 1 hour 30 minutes

Questions 3–10

Complete the notes below.

Write **NO MORE THAN TWO WORDS AND/OR A NUMBER** *for each answer.*

What is the teacher's name?	*John York*
How old is he?	3 ....
Where was he born?	4 ....
Is he married?	5 ....
What is his address?	6 ....
Which sport does he like best?	7 ....
Which languages does he speak?	*English*
	8 ....
	9 ....
What is his favourite food?	10 ....

SECTION 2

Questions 11–13

Choose the correct letter (A, B or C).

11 Which day is the trip?
    A Tuesday
    B Wednesday
    C Thursday

12 What time does the bus leave?
    A 07.15
    B 07.30
    C 07.45

13 How much is a student ticket?
    A £12
    B £15
    C £20

Questions 14 and 15

Choose TWO letters (A–E).

Which two things does the museum have?

    A restaurant

    B garden

    C cinema

    D gift shop

    E audio guide

14 ....

15 ....

Questions 16–20

Complete the table below.

Write **NO MORE THAN TWO WORDS** *for each answer.*

Room	Origin	Exhibits
Green Room	Italian	paintings
Blue Room	**16**	drawings
Red Room	English	**17** ....
18 .... Room	Japanese	ceramics
Orange Room	**19**	maps
White Room	Brazilian	**20** ....

SECTION 3

Questions 21 and 22

Complete the sentences below.

Write **NO MORE THAN TWO WORDS** *for each answer.*

Ben and Anna like travelling.

They usually go on holiday in the month of **21** ....

They like to plan their holiday very carefully.

They usually travel by **22** ....

Questions 23–30

Who usually does these things? (A = Anna, B = Ben, C = Both of them)

*Write the correct letter (**A**, **B** or **C**) next to questions 23–30.*

23 plans the route ....

24 books hotels ....

25 chooses where to eat ....

26 decides when to have a break ....

27 answers messages ....

28 goes shopping ....

29 takes photos ....

30 writes their blog ....

SECTION 4

Questions 31–35

Complete the sentences below.

*Write **NO MORE THAN THREE WORDS** for each answer.*

LION WORKSHEET

Lions live on the continents of Africa and **31** ....

A wild lion usually lives for **32** .... years.

Usually between one and **33** .... baby lions are born at the same time.

Lions often rest for **34** .... hours each day.

When there is food, the **35** .... lion eats first.

Questions 36–40

Complete the notes below.

*Write **NO MORE THAN THREE WORDS** for each answer.*

COUNTRY	SPORT	NAME
UK and Ireland	**36**	the Lions
Malta	**37**	Sannat Lions
38	cricket	Highveld Lions
39	ice hockey	Lac St Louis Lions
Ireland	**40**	Dublin Lions

READING TEST

SECTION 1

Questions 1–16

You should spend about 20 minutes on Questions 1–16.

Questions 1–10

*Look at the six advertisements for restaurants (**A–F**).*

*Match each statement with the correct restaurant. Write the correct letter (**A–F**) next to sentences 1–10.*

You can use any letter more than once.

1　You can only eat here in the evening.

2　You can eat food from many countries here.

3　The fish is very good here.

4　This restaurant is good for people who don't like meat.

5　You don't pay very much here.

6　This place is very quiet.

7　You can't eat here on Mondays.

8　You can only pay in cash here.

9　Local people like this place.

10　You can sometimes listen to music here.

A

Rose Restaurant

Open Monday–Friday lunchtimes only

Local English cooking
Famous for its excellent seafood
Wide range of meat dishes
Popular with tourists – can get very busy

All major credit cards accepted

B

Riverside Diner

Open every day of the week

Great breakfasts, lunches and dinners

Typical American food (burgers, fried chicken, etc.)

Live band in the evening at weekends

Very low prices

C

Jade Garden

Open Monday to Saturday only

Excellent Chinese food

Popular with office workers at lunchtime

Very busy at weekends – book a table!

No cheques or credit cards accepted

D

Joe's Place

Open every day from 19.00

Typical Italian cooking

Fantastic pizzas and pasta

Popular with international students

Fun place to eat – lots of noise!

E

Tamarind Café

Open Tuesday to Sunday

Mid-price international menu

Famous for its vegetable curry

Open for lunches and dinner

Quite expensive, but excellent food

F

Symond's

Open weekday lunchtimes
and Fri–Sun evenings

Beef and lamb a speciality

No vegetarian menu

Enjoy a relaxing meal in peaceful
surroundings

Most credit cards accepted

Questions 11–16

Read the text on the next page. It has six sections (A–F).

Choose the correct heading for each section from the list of headings below. Write the correct number (i–ix) next to numbers 11–16.

List of headings
i   what you can study
ii   sports facilities
iii   useful addresses
iv   exam dates and fees
v   finding a place to stay
vi   jobs at the college
vii   how to find us
viii   term dates
ix   how to apply for a course

11 SECTION **A**   ....

12 SECTION **B**   ....

13 SECTION **C**   ....

14 SECTION **D**   ....

15 SECTION **E**   ....

16 SECTION **F**   ....

Schofield College

Welcome to the Schofield College website.
Click on the links below to find out more about us.

SECTION A

Schofield College is located on Norman Street in the city of Schofield in the English Midlands. The nearest airport is at Birmingham (35 miles). Schofield is approximately 100 miles from London. Schofield College is in the city centre, just a few minutes' walk from the train station. The number 4A bus stops outside, and links the college with the shopping centre and the main residential districts.

SECTION B

The college runs courses in a range of subjects. There are English language classes for international students who wish to apply for a place at a British university and need to take the IELTS test. The college also offers courses for people who want to learn how to do jobs like hairdressing, motor-vehicle maintenance and hotel work. Most of the courses begin in late September and run for nine months.

SECTION C

Many college students already live in Schofield with their families. But there is residential accommodation available on campus for international students and anyone who lives too far away to travel to college every day. The rooms are in self-catering apartments, with shared use of a bathroom and kitchen. Contact Fiona Delyn, the Accommodation Officer (delyn@schocoll.org), for more information.

SECTION D

The college has a well-equipped gym and fitness centre, which students can use free of charge, and there are tennis courts on campus, which can be booked for a small fee. The college also has both men's and women's football teams which play in the nearby park. The women's team won the inter-college championship last year. If you are interested in playing, contact the coach, Barry Letts (letts@schocoll.org), and he will give you the dates and times of the training sessions.

SECTION E

If you'd like to study at the college, then please come along to our open day on 1 September. You can enrol for courses in the period 1–10 September. To get an application form, call in at Reception at 34 Norman Street, or you can complete the form online. If you need help with the form, contact Simon Groot, the Enrolment Officer (groot@schocoll.org). He will be happy to help you.

SECTION F

The college is also a major employer in the city, and there are regular vacancies in both the administration and catering departments. If you would like to find out more about working at the college, contact Rosa Smiles, the Recruitment Officer (smiles@schocoll.org), for more information. Schofield College is an equal-opportunities employer.

SECTION 2

You should spend about 20 minutes on Questions 17–27.

Read the text and answer questions 17–27.

Working in the community

Working with people is very interesting. People like nurses, police officers and teachers do important work in the community. We ask three people about their jobs.

Amelia (22) Nurse

I work in the surgical ward at the hospital. When I arrive in the morning, I go to see my patients and give them their medicine. I help the patients to get up, to have a wash and to get dressed. But I don't serve their meals – the catering staff do that. After breakfast, I make sure that patients are ready for their operations. I talk to them as they wait for their time to go to the operating theatre. When they come back after their operations, I am there to care for them.

My job can be very busy and very stressful. But because I'm helping people, I feel happy and satisfied at the end of the day. In my job, it's important to ask for help when you need it. You also need good communication skills.

To a young person who wants to be a nurse, I would say: 'Try working as a volunteer first. Then you can be sure that it is the best type of work for you.'

Amelia did a three-year diploma in nursing at Middlesex University. She earns £20,000 per year.

Contact **www.nhscareers.nhs.uk** for more information about careers in nursing.

- -

Benedict (27) Police Officer

I work at the police station. When people are arrested, my job is to stay with them, interview them and take notes. I start work at 7 am and sometimes I'm there until midnight. But I usually work an eight-hour shift. Some days are very busy – especially when I work at weekends. In my job, every day is different and that is why I like it. Sometimes I have to go to court with the prisoners, so I am not in the police station all the time. I started this job two years ago. Before that, I drove a police car. That was exciting. I arrested lots of people, usually bad drivers! But I never knew what happened to them after I took them to the police station. So, my new job is more interesting.

To a young person who wants to be a police officer, I would say: 'Go for it. It's a great life.'

Benedict joined the police force five years ago. He did eighteen weeks' basic training at police college. Before that, he worked as a computer salesman. He earns £27,000 per year. Benedict would like to become a police inspector one day.

Contact **www.met-police.tmpw.co.uk** for more information about careers in the police force.

- -

Connie (35) Teacher

I'm a science teacher in a secondary school. I am also responsible for all the computers and computer systems in the school. I teach science and I really love working with young people. My job can be stressful – because students always have a lot of questions about science and there are not always simple answers to give them. When the computer systems stop working, it is my job to solve the problem. That is really exciting. I am always busy. After school finishes, I hold a computer club for students. It's great fun, but we don't play games!

To a young person who wants to be a teacher, I would say: 'Make sure you know your subject very well.'

Connie did a three-year degree course in science at university and then spent a year at a teacher training college. She earns £25,000 per year. She designed a new website for her school last year. She hopes everyone will like using it.

Contact **www.canteach.gov.uk** for more information about careers in teaching.

Questions 17–19

*Choose the correct letter (**A–D**).*

17 Amelia doesn't help her patients to
    A put on their clothes.
    B use the bathroom.
    C get out of bed.
    D eat their food.

18 Benedict usually works
    A only at weekends.
    B seven hours a day.
    C eight hours a day.
    D after midnight.

19 What does Connie do after school hours?
    A She runs a computer club.
    B She plays computer games.
    C She fixes computer problems.
    D She designs websites on her computer.

Questions 20–27

Look at the statements (20–27) and the list of people below.

Match each statement with the correct person (A = Amelia, B = Benedict, C = Connie).

*Write the correct letter (**A, B** or **C**) next to numbers 20–27.*

Which person

worked as a driver in the past?	**20** ....
didn't study at university?	**21** ....
studied at two different places?	**22** ....
hopes to get a better job?	**23** ....
helps people before and after something?	**24** ....
can't always answer people's questions?	**25** ....
studied for a diploma before starting this job?	**26** ....
writes down the answers to questions?	**27** ....

Questions 28–30

Complete the sentences below.

*Choose **NO MORE THAN FOUR WORDS** from the passage for each answer.*

Which part of the hospital does Amelia work in?	**28** ....
Where does Benedict sometimes take prisoners?	**29** ....
Which website tells you about working in a school?	**30** ....

SECTION 3

Read the text and answer questions 31–40.

Billy Smith loves water. It's his passion! His hobbies are swimming and scuba diving. He likes golf too. Billy's a very lucky man. His interests are part of his job.

Billy lives in the USA with his wife, Linda. They were married ten years ago. At that time, Billy worked in an office in New York. He worked with computers. He worked five days a week, from eight in the morning to seven in the evening. He hated his job. There was no time for diving or golf. Linda worked in a shop and she didn't like her boss. She hated the cold winters in New York too. So, Billy and Linda decided to leave their jobs in New York and to buy a house in Florida. You can go diving in Florida, and there are lots of golf courses there. Linda was very happy too. The weather is fantastic in Florida. The days are sunny and hot.

Billy goes diving every day and he goes to golf courses every day. But he doesn't play golf very much – he works at golf courses now. He travels around Florida and he goes to lots of different golf courses. Sometimes Linda goes with him and sometimes she stays at home. There are lakes on many golf courses and Billy only goes to golf courses with lakes. Players often hit their golf balls into the water. Many balls go into the lakes and the golfers cannot find them again.

In his new job, Billy dives in the lakes for these golf balls. On some days, Billy collects two thousand golf balls. Linda has an office in their home and she works there. She sells the lost golf balls that Billy finds. The golf balls are not expensive. For golfers, they are cheaper than new golf balls.

Both Billy and Linda are very happy now. Linda is her own boss and a golf course is Billy's office!

Questions 31–37

Do the following statements agree with the information given in the text?

Write

TRUE	*if the statement agrees with the information*
FALSE	*if the statement contradicts the information*
NOT GIVEN	*if there is no information on this*

31 Billy is very good at golf.

32 Billy is married.

33 Billy liked working in an office.

34 Billy and his wife left New York eight years ago.

35 Linda works at a golf course.

36 Billy plays golf every day.

37 Billy doesn't work in an office now.

Questions 38–40

Complete the sentences below.

*Choose **ONE WORD** or **NUMBER** from the text for each answer.*

Billy worked with **38** .... in New York.

Billy dives in **39** .... to find golf balls.

Linda only sells **40** .... golf balls.

WRITING TEST

TASK 1

You should spend 20 minutes on this task.

> You are not well and can't go to college today.
>
> Write an email to your teacher. In your email:
> - tell the teacher that you are sorry.
> - say why you can't go to college.
> - ask what to do for homework.

Write about 150 words.

You do not need to write any addresses.

Begin your email like this:

Dear …

TASK 2

You should spend 40 minutes on this task.

Write about this topic.

> Some people say it is bad to eat fast food every day.
> What do you think?

Give reasons for your answer and include any relevant examples from your own knowledge or experience.

Write about 250 words.

SPEAKING TEST

PART 1: INTRODUCTION AND INTERVIEW

Let's talk about your home.

- Where do you live?
- Do you live in a big house?
- Who lives there with you?
- Do you like your house? Why? / Why not?

PART 2: INDIVIDUAL LONG TURN

Candidate Task Card

Talk about where you go shopping.

You should say:

- which shops you go to.

- who goes shopping with you.

- what you buy at the shops.

And explain why you like the shops you go to.

You will have to talk about the topic for one to two minutes.

You will have one minute to think about what you are going to say.

You can make some notes to help you if you wish.

Rounding-off questions

- Do you buy things on the internet? Why? / Why not?
- Where do you buy food?

PART 3: TWO-WAY DISCUSSION

Let's talk about the type of clothes you like to buy.

- Do you like buying clothes?
- How expensive are clothes in this country?
- Do you buy fashionable clothes? Why? / Why not?

Finally, let's talk about eating in restaurants.

- Why are some restaurants good and other restaurants not good?

Audioscripts

Unit 1

🔊 1

A B C D E F G H I J K L M N O P Q R S T U V W X Y Z

🔊 2

1	E	4	H	7	Q
2	I	5	K	8	W
3	J	6	S		

🔊 3

1   D–double O–R: door
2   C–H–A–I–R: chair
3   B–double O–K: book
4   D–E–S–K: desk
5   W–I–N–D–O–W: window
6   B–O–A–R–D: board

🔊 4

1   L–I–S–T–E–N: listen
2   L–double O–K: look
3   R–E–A–D: read
4   R–E–P–E–A–T: repeat
5   S–A–Y: say
6   W–R–I–T–E: write

🔊 5

W = woman, M = man
1   W1:   Hi. I'm Rosa.
     M1:   Hello, Rosa.
2   W2:   Hello! You're Paul!
     M2:   Yes! I'm Paul Freeman.
3   W3:   Hello. I'm Angela. I'm a teacher.
     W4:   Nice to meet you, Angela.
4   M4:   Hi. Nice to meet you.
     M4:   Oh, you're Jason Smith!

🔊 6

1	Russian	5	Italy
2	Egypt	6	Mexico
3	Brazilian	7	Vietnamese
4	Canadian		

🔊 8

This is Enzo Chellini. He's a painter. He's from Venice. Venice is in Italy. Enzo is Italian.

🔊 9

Hello! I'm Bruno. I'm a student. This is Astrid. She's a student too. She's from Hamburg. I'm from Toronto. It's in Canada.

🔊 10

| 1 | Good morning. | 3 | Good evening. |
| 2 | Good afternoon. | 4 | Good night. |

🔊 11

A = Anna, B = Barbara, C = Carlos
1   A: Good afternoon, Barbara. How are you?
     B: Fine, thanks. And you?
     A: I'm OK.
2   C: See you later, Anna.
     A: Bye, Carlos.

🔊 12

1   Lisa is Mexican. She's a student in Merida. Her family is in Mexico City. Her phone number is 55 018 375.
2   N: Hi. I'm Nasser. I'm from Egypt. I'm an engineer. I'm in London. My family is in Egypt. My phone number is 203 903 7529.
3   Boris is a writer. He's from Germany. His office is in New York. His mobile number is 707 839 116.

🔊 13

L = Lisa, B = Boris
L: Hi, Boris.
B: Hi, Lisa.
L: What's your phone number?
B: My mobile number is 707 839 116. My work number is 707 547 939.

L: Thanks.
B: What's your home number?
L: My home number is 55 018 375.
B: Great. Thanks.

🔊 14

S = student, T = teacher
1   S: What's this in English?
     T: It's a computer.
     S: Thanks.
2   S: Good afternoon. Sorry I'm late.
     T: That's OK.
3   T: Work in pairs.
     S: I don't understand.
     T: Work in pairs – two students.
4   T: OK. Open your books. Look at page ten.
     S: Page ten?
     T: Yes.
5   S: Can you repeat that, please?
     T: Yes. Look at page ten.
6   T: Good morning, everyone. Sit down, please.
     S: Good morning.
7   T: This is a table.
     S: Can you spell it, please?
     T: T–A–B–L–E.
8   T: Do Exercise three at home. See you next time.
     S: Bye.

🔊 15

1   What's this in English?
2   Can you repeat that, please?
3   Can you spell it, please?

🔊 16

Robert Smith   London   Brazil   Canadian   French

🔊 17

1   Q: What's your name?
     C: My name's Chris Cavendish.
4   Q: Can you spell that?
     C: Yes. C–A–V–E–N–D–I–S–H.
7   Q: How are you?
     C: I'm fine.
8   Q: What's your phone number?
     C: It's 96 457 329.

Unit 2

🔊 18

I'm on holiday. I'm with Linda, Will and Maria. They're my friends. We're in South America. This is Lake Titicaca. It's in Bolivia. It's beautiful.

🔊 19

1	We're on a beach.	4	We're English.
2	They're on a lake.	5	We're in Fiji.
3	They're Canadian.	6	They're in Portugal.

🔊 20

1	We're from Portugal.	4	We're on an island.
2	They're in a city.	5	They're in Canada.
3	They're Kenyan.	6	We're on Lake Titicaca.

🔊 21

1   This isn't in Europe.
2   I'm not in this photo.
3   The four tourists aren't Bolivian.
4   The man isn't a tourist.
5   We aren't in Thailand.
6   You aren't in this photo.

🔊 22

It's thirty-three degrees in Berlin today.
It's thirty degrees in Paris today.
It's thirty-seven degrees in Rio de Janeiro today.
It's eighteen degrees in Sydney today.
It's twenty-nine degrees in Toronto today.

23

1 A: Are you in London?
   B: No, I'm not.
2 A: Are you in a city?
   B: Yes, I am.
3 A: Is it hot today?
   B: No, it isn't.
4 A: Are you from Asia?
   B: Yes, I am.
5 A: Is your teacher English?
   B: No, he isn't.
6 A: Are your friends students?
   B: Yes, they are.

24

1 Are you in London?   4 Are you from Asia?
2 Are you in a city?   5 Is your teacher English?
3 Is it hot today?   6 Are your friends students?

25

Hi Stephanie
I'm in New Zealand. It's cold. The mountains are white.
The sky isn't blue – it's grey. I'm in a hotel. I'm with my
friend Kiri. It's nice.

26

buses tents cars cities offices photos beaches countries
friends hotels islands mountains

27

1 A: Where are you from?
   B: I'm from Belfast.
2 A: What's your address?
   B: It's 27 Front Street.
3 A: Is this your email address?
   B: No, it isn't. It's mross@gmail.com.
4 A: What's the car registration number?
   B: It's LE61 DGM.

28

J = Julia Farrow, A = assistant
J: Good morning. I'm Julia Farrow.
A: Good morning. What's your address, Ms Farrow?
J: It's 17 North Street.
A: 17 or 70?
J: 17. 17 North Street.
A: And is that in Manchester?
J: Yes, it is.
A: And what's the postcode?
J: It's M19 2GR.
A: What's your email address?
J: It's julia21@gmail.com.
A: OK. And is this your phone number … 0794 276 809?
J: Erm, 0794 276 809 … yes, it is.
A: OK. Here's your car key.

29

1 Where are you from?   3 What's the postcode?
2 What's your address?   4 What's your email address?

31

R = receptionist, D = Diana Black
R: Good morning. Lakeside Hotel.
D: Good morning. It's about my hotel booking.
R: What's your name, please?
D: It's Diana Black.
R: Is that Ms or Mrs?
D: It's Mrs.
R: And what's your address?
D: 26 Hill Street.
R: And the city?
D: London.
R: And what's the postcode?
D: It's SW18 3ND.
R: What's your email address?
D: It's d.black@gmail.com.
R: OK. And what's your phone number?
D: 0750 658 214.
R: Thanks. OK, Mrs Black, one moment.

Unit 3

33

J = Jack
J: Hi. My name's Jack. This is my family. This is Jamie. He's my
brother. This is Jenna. She's my sister. This is Jane. She's my
mother. And this is Jerry. He's my father. We're from Ireland.

34

J = Jane
J: Hello. My name's Jane. This is Jenna. She's my daughter.
These are my sons, Jamie and Jack. My parents are Patrick
and Moira.

35

1 My name's Sol. My eyes are brown.
2 Is your dad old?
3 That's Kei. He's tall!
4 She's Petra. She's a young tennis player.
5 Hi. I'm Stan. My hair is red.
6 That's Tom Cruise. He's short.

36

1 It's Sarah's notebook.
2 It's Eva's bag.
3 They're Ahmed's pencils.
4 It's Felipe's computer.
5 They're Claude's pens.
6 It's Enzo's phone.

37

1 A: How old are you, Kate?
   B: I'm twenty-nine.
2 A: How old is your husband?
   B: He's twenty-eight.
3 A: How old are your parents?
   B: My father is sixty-five and my mother is fifty-nine.
4 A: How old is your daughter?
   B: She's seven years old.

38

1 Where are your parents from?
2 What's your mother's name?
3 What's your father's job?
4 What's your friend's phone number?
5 Where's your teacher from?
6 Who are your friends in your English class?

39

1 When's your birthday?
2 How old are you?
3 How old is your best friend?
4 When's his or her birthday?

40

In the United Kingdom, seven per cent of the people
are not British. In Luxembourg, half of the people are
not from Luxembourg. They are from one hundred and
seventy countries! Forty per cent of the people are from the
European Union (EU).
In Iceland, six per cent of the people are from EU countries.
These people are young. The average age is thirty years old.
In Spain, five per cent of the people are from EU countries.
They aren't old. The average age is thirty-two years old.

41

1 A: Happy Birthday!
   B: Thank you!
   A: How old are you today?
   B: I'm ninety-five!
   A: Wow!
2 C: Twenty-one today!
   D: Yes, that's right. I'm twenty-one!
   C: Here's a present for you.
   D: Oh, thank you.
3 E: And this is Naomie.
   F: Ah, she's beautiful. Congratulations!
   E: Thank you. We're very happy.
4 G: Mum! Dad! Happy New Year!
   M: And to you too!

42
1   Congratulations!
2   Happy Birthday!
3   Happy New Year!

43
1   A: Hello, Maria. This is for you and Oscar.
     M: Oh, thank you very much.
     A: You're welcome.
2   B: Hi, Daisy. Come in!
     D: This is for you.
     B: Oh, that's very kind.

44
1   This is our new baby!
2   I'm 21 today.
3   Here's a present for you.
4   Happy New Year, everyone!

45
1   We're very happy!
2   What's your brother's name?
3   It isn't my wedding today.
4   How old are you?
5   What's your address?
6   My cousins are at home.

Unit 4

47
1   A: Excuse me?
     B: Yes?
     A: Where's the Express Café?
     B: It's in Kent Street. It's next to the museum.
     A: OK. Thanks.
2   C: Excuse me?
     D: Yes?
     C: Is the bus station in this street?
     D: No, it isn't. This is Kent Street. The bus station's in Norfolk Street. It's next to the cinema.
     C: Thank you very much.
3   E: Excuse me. Is the market near here?
     F: Yes, it is. It's in Kent Street. It's opposite the museum.
     E: OK. Thanks.
4   G: Excuse me?
     H: Yes?
     G: Is the bank near here?
     H: Yes, it is. It's in Norfolk Street. It's next to the information centre.
     G: OK. Thanks.

48
1   The cinema is next to the bus station.
2   The museum is in Norfolk Street.
3   The market is near the bus station.
4   The cinema is opposite the café.

49
1   Excuse me. Is the market near here?
2   Excuse me. Is the bank near here?
3   Excuse me. Where's the cinema?
4   Excuse me. Where's the Express Café?

51
W: Excuse me. What's the name of this street?
M: It's Newbury Street.
W: OK. Thanks. Is the Old Market in this street?
M: No, it isn't. It's in Main Street.
W: Where's that?
M: It's in the centre of the village.
W: Is it on the map?
M: Yes … here.
W: Great. Is it open today?
M: No, it isn't. Today's Monday.
W: When's it open?
M: Every day, but not Monday!

52
1   What time is it, please?
2   Excuse me, what time is it?
3   What time is it?
4   Excuse me, what time is it?
5   What time is it, please?
6   What time is it?

53
1   The City Park is open every day from nine in the morning to eight in the evening.
2   The City Bank is open from Monday to Friday. It is open from nine o'clock to three thirty.
3   The Royal Cinema is open every day. It is open from five in the evening to midnight.
4   The Italia Café isn't open on Tuesday.

55
A = assistant, C = customer
1   A: Hi. Can I help you?
     C: Two cakes, please.
     A: Anything else?
     C: No, thanks.
     A: OK. Five euros, please.
2   A: Hi. Can I help you?
     C: Can I have a coffee, please?
     A: Large or small?
     C: Large.
     A: Anything else?
     C: No, thanks.
3   A: Can I help you?
     C: A mineral water and two teas, please.
     A: Anything else?
     C: Yes. A fruit juice.
     A: OK. Here you are. Eight euros, please.
     C: Here you are.

57
1   Can I help you?   4   Large or small?
2   Can I help you?   5   Anything else?
3   Can I help you?   6   Anything else?

Unit 5

58
1   This robot can play football.   4   People can run.
2   Children can't fly.   5   Babies can see.
3   Babies can't speak.   6   People can speak.

59
1   This robot can see.   4   My sister can speak Arabic.
2   I can't fly.   5   Robots can help people.
3   This robot can't run.   6   My friend can't speak Chinese.

60
1   Can you speak English?   4   Can you swim?
2   Can you speak Chinese?   5   Can you cook?
3   Can you play the piano?   6   Can you drive a car?

61
1   I have three sisters.
2   My friend has a VW car.
3   In my family, we have two cats.
4   My sister has four children.
5   My classmates have dictionaries.
6   My brother has a guitar and a piano.

62
I have a lot of things in my bag. It's big! So, number one – my ***. It's new. I can take great photos of my friends and family now. Number two – my ***. I can't read or drive without my ***. They're brown. Number three – my ***. This is the key for my house, this is the key for my car and this is the key for my parents' house. Number four – my ***. It isn't new. It's about three years old. It has a camera, but it isn't very good. Number five – my ***. It's nice. It's expensive – a present from my parents. Oh, and I have a bottle of water too.

63

R = Ryan (presenter), S = Sara (guest)

R: Hello again. This is the *Technology* programme on Radio 4. I'm Ryan Watts and today my guest is Sara Brown. Sara has some news about a very unusual bike. Sara, tell us about the Aquaduct bike.

S: Well, the Aquaduct bike has a seat, pedals and three wheels.

R: Three wheels?

S: Yes, that's right. And it has two water tanks.

R: Oh?

S: Yes, this bike can carry water. It has a big water tank and a small water tank.

R: OK. And why is that?

S: Well, in a lot of places in the world, the water isn't very clean. You can't drink it. This bike can make the water clean.

R: Is it expensive?

S: Well, at the moment you can't buy it. This is a new design. But it's a really good idea for people in poor parts of the world.

64

1 A: How much is this?
   B: It's twenty-seven euros.
2 A: How much is it?
   B: That's fifteen pounds, please.
3 A: How much is this?
   B: It's seventy dollars.
4 A: How much is it?
   B: That's eighty-five real, please.
5 A: How much is this?
   B: It's fifty-eight dirham.
6 A: How much is this?
   B: It's nine hundred yen.

65

1 A: How much is this?
   B: It's thirty pounds.
2 A: How much is this?
   B: It's fourteen pounds fifty.
3 A: How much are these?
   B: They're sixteen pounds sixty.
4 A: How much is this?
   B: It's seventeen pounds eighty-five.
5 A: How much are these?
   B: They're eighty pounds twenty.
6 A: How much is this?
   B: It's ninety pounds ninety-nine.

68

A = assistant, C = customer

A: Can I help you?
C: Yes. How much are these memory sticks?
A: They're nineteen euros.
C: Hmm, that's a bit expensive. How much is this camera?
A: It's ninety-five euros.
C: OK. I'd like this camera, please.
A: Certainly.
C: Can I pay with a card?
A: Yes, of course.

69

A = assistant, C = customer

A: Can I help you?
C: How much are these speakers?
A: They're forty-nine pounds.
C: OK. And how much is this alarm clock?
A: It's twelve ninety-five.
C: OK. I'd like this alarm clock and the speakers, please.
A: That's sixty-one ninety-five, please.
C: Can I pay with euros?
A: Yes, of course.
C: Here you are.

Unit 6

70

1 Do you like tennis?
2 Do you like football?
3 Do you like swimming?
4 Do you like cycling?
5 Do you like Formula 1?
6 Do you like basketball?

71

1 The Olympic Games has about 300 sports events.
2 About 200 countries are in the Olympic Games.
3 About 10,000 people are in the Olympic Games.
4 The population of the United Kingdom is 65,000,000 people.
5 Football is the national sport in Brazil. The population of Brazil is 210,000,000 people.

72

1 I like animals. I like fish and birds.
2 My favourite TV shows are wildlife and reality shows.
3 I like films, but I don't like action films. I like comedies.
4 I like music. I like jazz and pop.
5 I like swimming, but scuba diving is my favourite sport.
6 I have a lot of books. I like detective stories and novels.

73

I = interviewer, A = Andrew

I: Hi, Andrew. Can I ask you some questions about your favourite things?
A: Yes, of course.
I: OK. What's your favourite animal?
A: Oh, I don't like animals very much.
I: Ah … OK. Do you like music?
A: Yes, I do.
I: What's your favourite kind of music?
A: I like jazz.
I: And what's your favourite TV show?
A: Well, I don't like wildlife shows … but I like reality shows. They're my favourite TV shows.
I: Do you like films?
A: Yes, I like comedies a lot.
I: What about action films?
A: No, I don't like them very much.
I: OK. And what's your favourite book?
A: Well, I like detective stories. I think my favourites are the Sherlock Holmes stories.
I: And finally, how about sports?
A: I don't like sports.
I: OK. Thanks very much for your time.

74

1 Andrew likes jazz.
2 Andrew's friend doesn't like jazz.
3 Emile likes scuba diving.
4 Emile doesn't like novels.
5 Frances doesn't like pop music.
6 Frances likes tennis.

75

I'm here in the stadium. It's fantastic. About 80,000 people are in the stadium. And for a lot of people, the British athlete Jonnie Peacock is the star here today. Peacock is passionate about sports and he's passionate about his sports event – running. Peacock has an artificial leg, but he can run fast. His event is the 100-metre race. OK, we are ready for the race. It's the final of the 100 metres.

76

1 Ugh, steak's horrible.
2 Look, it's the tennis final. They're great players.
3 Oh, this music is fantastic. I love it.
4 Oh, not Formula 1! It's really boring.

78

1 Do you like steak?
2 Do you like tennis?
3 Do you like pop music?
4 Do you like Formula 1?
5 Do you like action films?
6 Do you like reality TV shows?

79

1 A: Let's play tennis this weekend.
    B: No, thanks. I don't like tennis. It's boring.
2 A: Do you like action films?
    B: Yes, they're fantastic.
    A: OK, well let's watch *Die Hard* tonight.
    B: That's an old film.
    A: Yes, but it's great. I love Bruce Willis.
3 A: Let's have fish tonight.
    B: Oh, I don't like fish. It's horrible!
    A: Well, how about pasta?
    B: That's a good idea.

80

1 A: Let's play tennis this weekend.
2 A: Do you like action films?
    A: OK, well let's watch *Die Hard* tonight.
    A: Yes, but it's great. I love Bruce Willis.
3 A: Let's have fish tonight.
    A: Well, how about pasta?

Unit 7

81

My name's Tommy. I work in Colorado in the United States. I have three teams of four men. We work 24 hours a day. I get up at half past six and I start work at seven o'clock. I don't have breakfast, but I have lunch at half past eleven. I'm at work in the afternoon until about half past five, when I finish work. In the evening, I like to meet my friends, Jeff and Bud, and I go to bed at eleven o'clock.

83

1 In my house, we get up at half past seven.
2 We have cereal for breakfast.
3 I don't eat meat.
4 I meet my friends in the evening.
5 I don't have lunch at home.
6 I go to bed at midnight.

84

1 Do you understand Kiswahili?
2 Do your friends make videos?
3 Do we have an internet connection?
4 Do your friends go to festivals?
5 Do they enjoy singing?
6 Do you listen to music?

85

1 I = interviewer, D = Danielle
    I: Danielle, what's your favourite time of year?
    D: Well, I like spring a lot. I meet my friends at the park and we go for walks or we just talk.
    I: What about summer? What do you do in summer?
    D: Oh, I like summer and hot weather because I can be outside. On sunny days, we eat lunch outside and of course we don't watch TV very much in summer – we're outside.
    I: So, when do you watch TV? In winter?
    D: Yes.
2 I = interviewer, C = Christopher
    I: Christopher, is summer your favourite season?
    C: No, I like summer and autumn. Autumn is great. I like the weather in autumn – it's windy and rainy.
    I: Where do you go on rainy days?
    C: I don't go out! On rainy days, I read books a lot. It's great. And we cook a lot.
    I: Who do you cook with?
    C: Oh, my sister. I live with my sister.
3 I = interviewer, P = Patrick
    I: Patrick, you play golf. Do you play all year?
    P: No, I don't. I don't play golf in winter.
    I: So, you don't like the weather in winter?
    P: Yes, I do. Snowy weather is fantastic.
    I: Why do you like snowy weather?
    P: Well, I take a lot of photos – it's a beautiful time of year.

86

1 A: What's the matter?
    B: I don't feel well.
    A: Are you cold?
    B: No, I'm hot.
    A: Hmm.
2 C: What's the matter?
    D: I'm tired.
    C: Why don't you go to bed?
    D: It's only nine o'clock!
3 E: Are you OK?
    F: No, I'm not. I'm thirsty.
    E: Why don't you have a cup of tea?
    F: No, thanks. I don't like tea.
    E: Well, have a drink of water!
4 G: What's the matter?
    H: I don't understand this magazine article. It's in French.
    G: Why don't you use a dictionary? Here you are.
    H: Oh, thanks.

88

1 I'm really thirsty.
2 I'm hungry.
3 I'm bored.
4 I don't understand this book.
5 I don't feel well.

Unit 8

89

1 What do you do?
2 Where do you work?
3 Who do you work with?
4 Do you work near your home?
5 Do you like your job?

90

R = Rajesh, A = Amelia
R: Oh dear.
A: What's the matter?
R: Oh, it's a text message from my friend Magnus.
A: Magnus … is he a doctor?
R: No, that's my friend Pauline. Pauline doesn't write text messages – she phones me.
A: So what's the problem with Magnus?
R: He doesn't like his new job. He's a police officer in London.
A: OK. Well, that's a difficult job.
R: Yes, it is. And he doesn't live in London. So he gets up early – about five o'clock in the morning – because he starts work at seven o'clock.
A: Five o'clock! That's early!
R: Yes. He goes to work on the train. It's about an hour.
A: What's his job in the police?
R: He drives a police car. I think he enjoys that. I think the problem is he doesn't know a lot of people in London.
A: OK. Let's meet him. Send him a message.
R: OK. Is Saturday night OK?
A: It's great!

91

1 A doctor works in a hospital.
2 My friend gets up at five thirty.
3 We start work at seven o'clock.
4 My friend and I watch TV in the evening.
5 My sister finishes work at ten thirty.
6 My friend goes to work on the train.

92

1 Pauline checks papers.
2 Amelia doesn't use a computer.
3 Lisa answers questions and helps people.
4 Kris doesn't work alone.
5 Jamal doesn't work in an office.
6 Bill sells snacks.

🔊 93

In square one, draw a board.
In square two, draw three pens.
In square three, write 'college'.
In square four, draw a teacher.
In square five, write 'university'.
In square six, draw two books.
In square seven, draw a student.
In square eight, write 'classroom'.
In square nine, draw a pencil.

🔊 94

1 Q: Does Majed go to college?
  A: No, he doesn't. He goes to secondary school.
2 Q: Does Tarik live in the capital?
  A: No, he doesn't. He lives in the mountains.
3 Q: Does Zahid like his school?
  A: Yes, he does.
4 Q: Does the school open every day?
  A: No, it doesn't. It doesn't open on Thursday and Friday.
5 Q: Does Majed study English?
  A: Yes, he does.
6 Q: Does Tarik have classes in English?
  A: No, he doesn't.

🔊 95

I = interviewer, M = Michel
I: Michel, you are a scientist at the sleep laboratory.
M: Yes, I am.
I: Why do you study sleep?
M: Because sleep is important. In some jobs, people work a lot of hours. For example, police officers often work twelve hours. They are tired at work. That isn't good. Or nurses change their work routine every week. They finish work and they're tired, but they can't sleep. We can help people, but we don't understand sleep well.
I: OK. And how do you study sleep?
M: People come to our laboratory. They sleep and we watch them.
I: Do you do experiments?
M: Yes, we do. For example, we change the light. We use different colours of light – blue light, red light.
I: And what are the results with the different colours?
M: Well, blue light usually wakes people up.
I: So is blue light good for a tired person at work?
M: Possibly. We aren't sure. We don't understand how it works.
I: OK, Michel, thank you very much.
M: You're welcome.

🔊 96

R = receptionist, C = caller
1 R: Hello, Life Laboratories. Can I help you?
  C: Good morning. Can I speak to Mr Simpson, please?
  R: Yes, one moment, please.
  C: Thank you.
2 R: Good morning, Life Laboratories. Can I help you?
  C: Yes, can I speak to Susana Barros, please?
  R: I'm sorry. She doesn't work in the mornings.
  C: OK, thank you. I'll call back later. Goodbye.
  R: Goodbye.

🔊 97

1 Good afternoon. Can I speak to Mr Smith, please?
2 Good morning. Can I speak to Jessica Weir, please?
3 Hi. Can I speak to Elizabeth Murray, please?
4 Good morning. Can I speak to Ms Roubini, please?
5 Good afternoon. Can I speak to David Brown, please?
6 Hi. Can I speak to Hassan, please?

🔊 100

1	boss	7	dinner	13	summer
2	businessman	8	engineer	14	tourist
3	call	9	finish	15	usually
4	college	10	meeting	16	week
5	different	11	midday		
6	difficult	12	sleep		

Unit 9

🔊 101

A: What's in *Travel 365* magazine this week?
B: Well, there are some unusual pyramids in Mexico. This one – Chichen Itza – is a World Heritage Site. And it has 365 steps!
A: Wow!
B: There's an amazing castle in Edinburgh too.
A: Can you visit it?
B: Yes, you can. There are some photos of Japan – there are some fantastic shops in Tokyo. They sell amazing gadgets.
A: I like Japan.
B: And there's an article on islands in Indonesia – there are some beautiful beaches. It's a good place for scuba diving.
A: OK.
B: And there are some beautiful old buildings in Russia.
A: Oh yes, in Moscow and in St Petersburg too. I love the Hermitage Museum.
B: And finally, there's a famous old prison in South Africa. It's on Robben Island. It's open to tourists now.

🔊 102

1 There are some unusual pyramids in Mexico.
3 There are some fantastic shops in Tokyo.
4 There are some beautiful beaches in Indonesia.
5 There are some beautiful old buildings in Russia.

🔊 105

1 There are four shirts in my suitcase.
2 They're red and white.
3 There are two pairs of trousers.
4 They're old.
5 There are three jumpers.
6 They're new.

🔊 106

A: The Hotel Miramar is nice.
B: Yes, but it's expensive. Are there any cheap hotels near the beach?
A: Yes, there are two or three. And there's a youth hostel too.
B: Is there a website for the youth hostel?
A: Let's see. I don't think so. No, there isn't. There's an email address and there's a phone number, but there isn't a website.
B: OK. What about that hotel – Golden Sands? Is there a website?
A: Yes, there is – but there aren't any free rooms.
B: Oh well. Let's send an email to the youth hostel.

🔊 107

There are two islands in New Zealand – the North Island and the South Island. You can drive from one end of the North Island to the other in about four days. It's a fantastic road trip. Why? Because this is the country of *The Lord of the Rings*. It's amazing. Start in Auckland and finish in Wellington, the capital. It's about 740 kilometres. In Auckland, there's a great museum. You can learn about the Maori people. On the road to Wellington you travel through mountains, forests and volcanoes too. Stop in Rotorua and visit the volcanoes and hot lakes. Don't stay in hotels – there are lots of bed and breakfast places, and they're cheap and friendly. When you arrive in Wellington, you can go on *The Lord of the Rings* tours of the city. It's a great road trip, but don't forget – in New Zealand people drive on the left of the road!

🔊 108

R = receptionist, G = guest
1 R: Good afternoon. Can I help you?
  G1: Hello. I'd like a room for tonight.
  R: Just one night?
  G1: Yes, just tonight.
  R: Certainly. Can I have your name, please?
  G1: It's Khan. Nuno Khan.
  R: And can I have your credit card?
  G1: Here you are.
2 G2: Hi. We're Mr and Mrs Jones. We have a reservation.
  R: Jones … of course … four nights?
  G2: Yes, that's right.
  R: OK. That's fine. Your room number is 258.

G2: OK. Can you help us with our bags?
R: Yes, of course.
3 R: Mr Khan, can I help you?
G1: Yes, please. Can you tell me the wi-fi password?
R: Of course. It's Miramar18. With a capital 'M'.
G1: Great. And I'd like to stay another night.
R: That's no problem.

🎵 110
1 Good afternoon. Can I help you?
2 Good afternoon. Can I help you?
3 Good afternoon. Can I help you?
4 Good afternoon. Can I help you?

Unit 10
🎵 111
1	two thousand and twelve	4	two thousand and five
2	nineteen ninety-one	5	fourteen ninety-two
3	eighteen thirty-six	6	seventeen seventy

🎵 112
1	1998	3	1875	5	1750
2	2000	4	2015	6	2008

🎵 113
1 the first of January
2 the fourth of July
3 the twelfth of August
4 the eighteenth of May
5 the twenty-second of February
6 the thirty-first of December

🎵 114
1 John Logie Baird was born in 1888.
2 He was an engineer and inventor.
3 He was the inventor of television.
4 His parents were from Scotland.
5 He was born in Scotland.
6 His children were born in England.

🎵 115
1 Irene Curie was born on 12th September 1897.
2 Eve Curie was born in 1904.
3 John Logie Baird was born in 1888.
4 Sally Ride was born on 26th May 1951.
5 Alfred Nobel was born on 21st October 1833.
6 Mao Zedong was born in 1893.

🎵 116
Q: Was your school big?
J: No, it wasn't. It was small.
Q: Were you good at science?
J: No, I wasn't. I was very bad at science.
Q: Were the teachers friendly?
J: No, they weren't. They were good, but they weren't friendly.
Q: Were the lessons interesting?
J: Yes, they were.
Q: Was your best friend in your class?
J: Yes, she was. Her name was Estelle.
Q: Were your classmates nice?
J: Yes, they were.

🎵 117
Q: Was your school big?
J: No, it wasn't.
Q: Were you good at science?
J: No, I wasn't.
Q: Were the teachers friendly?
J: No, they weren't.
Q: Were the lessons interesting?
J: Yes, they were.
Q: Was your best friend in your class?
J: Yes, she was.
Q: Were your classmates nice?
J: Yes, they were.

🎵 118
1 Was your school big?
2 Were you good at science?
3 Were the teachers friendly?
4 Were the lessons interesting?
5 Was your best friend in your class?
6 Were your classmates nice?

🎵 119
P = presenter, H = historian
P: Let's see, this is an interesting picture.
H: Yes, it's from a document from about 1540.
P: And who was this man?
H: Well, he was an Aztec leader.
P: Was he from Peru?
H: No, he wasn't. The Aztecs weren't from Peru. They lived in the area we call Mexico today.
P: Oh, of course. And what was this leader's name?
H: There are different spellings of his name – Moctezuma and Montezuma, for example.
P: So, the picture is from a document from 1540. But when was he born?
H: We think he was born about 1466 and we know he died in 1520.
P: Why was he an important ruler?
H: Well, he was the ruler from 1502 to 1520 and that's when the Aztec Empire was very big and important.

🎵 120
1 Q: Where were you this morning?
M: I'm sorry, I wasn't well.
2 Q: Where were you this morning?
W: I'm sorry, I was on the phone.
3 Q: Where were you this morning?
W: I'm sorry, I was in traffic.
4 Q: Where were you this morning?
M: I'm sorry, I was asleep.
5 Q: Where were you this morning?
M: I'm sorry, I was at home.
6 Q: Where were you this morning?
W: I'm sorry, I was busy.

🎵 121
1 T: Hi. Where were you this morning?
S: I'm sorry. I was at home.
T: OK, but why were you at home?
S: I wasn't well.
T: Oh dear!
S: Don't worry. I'm OK now, thanks.
2 P: Hello!
C: Hi, Paul. I'm sorry I'm late. There was a traffic jam.
P: That's OK. Don't worry. I was late too.
3 F: Hello, Jake.
J: Hi! Where were you last night?
F: Oh, I'm very sorry.
J: We were all at the restaurant.
F: I was busy at work. There were a lot of phone calls.
J: OK.

🎵 122
1	I was at home.	4	I was late too.
2	I wasn't well.	5	I'm very sorry.
3	I'm sorry I'm late.	6	I was busy at work.

🎵 123
1 Where were you last night?
2 Where were you last night?
3 Where were you this morning?
4 Where were you last night?
5 Where were you this morning?
6 Where were you this morning?

Unit 11
🎵 124
1 I took a bus to town.
2 I went to work.
3 We had a bad evening.
4 A customer found a snail in his food.

🎵 125
1 When I was young, we lived in a small house.
2 When I was five years old, I started school.
3 My grandfather died at the age of ninety-one.

4   We studied history and science at school.
5   I walked to my English class yesterday.
6   We finished Unit 10 last week.

126
1   Did you write your diary at university?
2   Did your wife go on your trips?
3   Did you drive to the South Pole?
4   Did you meet interesting people?
5   Did your children read your diaries?
6   Did you write a book last year?

127
1   Did you read a book last weekend?
2   Did you fly around the world last year?
3   When was your last holiday?
4   Did you watch TV last night?
5   What was the last film you saw?
6   Did your friends visit you last weekend?

128
So, one day on the expedition, the weather was really bad. It was snowy and windy. There was snow on the ice and on the sea. The two men walked across the ice. Then the ice broke and Mike Horn fell into the sea. The sea was very cold. Borge Ousland helped him. But Horn was cold and wet. His clothes were wet. This was very dangerous. Ousland started a fire. They dried Horn's clothes. Then they walked across the ice again. After two hours, Horn fell into the sea again. It was a very bad day.

129
1   A: Did you have a nice meal on Saturday?
    B: No, we didn't.
    A: Oh? Why not?
    B: I found a snail in my food!
    A: Oh dear! What did you do?
    B: We left the restaurant and we didn't pay!
2   C: Did you have a nice holiday?
    D: Yes, thanks, we did.
    C: Where did you go?
    D: We went to the Red Sea. It was beautiful.
    C: Did you go scuba diving?
    D: Well, we didn't go scuba diving, but we went swimming.
3   E: Did you have a good trip last week?
    F: No, I didn't.
    E: Oh? Why not?
    F: The weather was really bad. I was at the airport for six hours.
    E: Six hours! What did you do?
    F: Nothing. I didn't have my laptop with me.

131
1   Did you have a good weekend?
2   What did you do?
3   Did you have a nice meal last night?
4   What did you eat?
5   Did you have a good holiday last year?
6   Where did you go?

Unit 12

132
1   The man is sitting on a chair.
2   The children are sitting on the floor.
3   The boy is looking at the camera.
4   The girl is standing near a small table. She is wearing a dress.

133
J = Joe, A = Ali
J: Hi Ali. What are you doing?
A: Nothing special. I'm watching TV.
J: What are you watching?
A: It's a programme about shopping.
J: OK.
A: Are you watching TV?
J: No, I'm not. Jack is here. We're playing a video game.
A: Oh! Is it good?
J: Yes, it is.

A: Wait for me. I'm coming to your house.
J: Now?
A: Yes. I'm leaving the house right now.
J: OK, great. See you soon.

134
1   Are you in the living room?
2   Are people watching TV in your house?
3   What are you wearing?
4   Are you sitting on a sofa?
5   Are you eating?

135
C = Carla, R = Rosa
C: Rosa, are you coming to the cinema tomorrow evening?
R: No, I'm not. We're going away for the weekend.
C: Oh?
R: Yes, Monday is a holiday. So we have three days.
C: Where are you going?
R: We're going to Edinburgh. It's the Edinburgh festival.
C: That's great. Are you leaving tomorrow?
R: No, we aren't. I'm working in the evening. So, we're taking the train on Saturday morning. We're going to a concert on Saturday evening. And then on Sunday, we're meeting friends. What about you? What are you doing?
C: I'm staying at home. I'm going shopping on Saturday because my sister is coming on Sunday. We're having lunch at home.
R: Is she getting married next year?
C: No, she's getting married next month! There's a lot to do!
R: Oh, yes!
C: Are you coming back from Edinburgh on Monday?
R: Yes, we are, on the last train!

136
1   What are you doing this weekend?
2   Are you going to the cinema tomorrow?
3   What are your friends doing tonight?
4   Where are you going on Sunday?

137
1   I'm very busy in my job. I travel every week. At the weekend, I relax. I go to the country. I go on special courses and I learn new things. I usually go every weekend. I go with friends. Last weekend I did a painting course. It was really great. I'm not very good at painting, but I like it. Next weekend I'm doing a yoga course.
2   I work in an office in Edinburgh. My job is a typical nine-to-five, Monday-to-Friday job. So at the weekend, I do adventure sports. I go to an adventure centre. I go on special courses and I learn new sports. I sometimes go with friends and I sometimes go alone. I meet people and make new friends. Last weekend I went canoeing on the river. It was fantastic. Next weekend I'm going mountain climbing.

138
1   A: Hi, Belinda. Come in.
    B: Hi. How are you?
    A: I'm fine. Would you like a drink? Tea or coffee?
    B: Yes, tea's great. Thanks.
    A: OK, just a moment.
2   C: Do you want to go to the cinema this week?
    D: Erm, which day?
    C: Friday evening?
    D: Sorry, I can't make it on Friday.
    C: OK. Do you want to go on Thursday?
    D: Yes, that's fine.
3   E: What are you doing this weekend?
    F: We're going to the mountains.
    E: Oh, I'd like to come.
    F: Great! Would you like to come in our car?
    E: Yes, please.

IELTS practice test

🔊 140

Presenter: In this test, you'll hear a number of different recordings and you'll have to answer questions on what you hear. There will be time for you to read the instructions and questions before you listen. You will also have time to check your work after you listen. In the IELTS listening test, you hear the recordings once only. The test is in five sections.

Now look at Section 1 on page 100 of your book. You will hear some information about English lessons. First, you have some time to look at questions 1 and 2. There is also an example which has been done for you.

Presenter: Now we shall begin. Answer the questions as you listen because you will not hear the recording a second time. Listen and answer questions 1 and 2.

Principal: Hello. I have some information about your English classes. Listen carefully. The college opens on Monday and all students do an English test. Your first lesson is on Tuesday. There are three levels: beginner, elementary and intermediate. If your lesson is too easy or too difficult, don't worry. You can try a different level on Wednesday.

Now, about the rooms. English lessons are usually held in rooms 14, 15 and 16. But when you go to do your test, please go to room 16. It's the only one that's big enough for everyone to sit and write at the same time.

English lessons usually last for one hour and thirty minutes. You have two lessons each morning with a twenty-minute break between them when you can buy coffee and snacks. Your English test only takes one hour and ten minutes, however. So you have time to look around the college on your first day.

Presenter: You will hear an English teacher talking to his class. First, you have some time to look at questions 3–10.

Presenter: Now listen and answer questions 3–10.

Teacher: Hello. Welcome. I am your English teacher. My name is John York. I want to tell you about myself.

First, my age. I am thirty-two years old and I have been a teacher for ten years. I like my job very much.

I wasn't born here in London – my family comes from the north of England and I was born in Manchester. That's where I lived when I was a child and I went to university there. I studied English literature and history.

My wife's name is Helen. We got married three years ago. We have a baby called Ronan. He is eighteen months old. He's lovely.

I live in the south-east of London. My address is 22 West Street. It takes me about 30 minutes to travel to work each day. I travel by train.

In my free time, I like playing sports. I can play tennis and football, but my favourite sport is golf. I play that every weekend. I am a member of the golf club.

I also like travelling and speaking other languages. I studied Spanish at school, and I can also speak Italian. Now I want to learn Chinese. My lessons begin this week. It's exciting because I am a student like you in that class – not the teacher! I hope it isn't too difficult!

I like all different types of food. Last week I tried Thai food for the first time. I liked it. But my favourite food is fried chicken. I eat that every week. The only food I don't like is fried fish. I don't know why, but I just don't like it.

Presenter: Now look at Section 2 on page 101 of your book. You will hear some information about a visit to a museum. First, you have some time to look at questions 11–13.

Presenter: Now listen and answer questions 11–13.

Teacher: Hello. I want to tell you about the college trip to the museum, so please listen carefully.

Remember we talked about going to a museum one day this week? Well, some people wanted to go on Tuesday, but that is a problem for me because there is a teachers' meeting here at lunchtime. So I asked the museum if we could go on Wednesday – and they said that the museum is closed on Wednesday afternoon. That leaves Thursday. I hope that's a good day for everyone.

Now, there is a bus to take you from the college to the museum. Please tell me if you want to take the bus. I know that some of you live near the museum, so you don't need to take the bus. We can all meet at the museum at nine o'clock. To catch the bus, please come to the college no later than seven forty-five. I told the driver to come at seven thirty and to wait for fifteen minutes. OK – so don't be late.

Remember, it costs more to go into the museum alone. In a student group, we only pay £12 each. Usually it costs £20 for adults and £15 for children. So we have a good price. But it's important for everyone to wait outside so that we can all go in together. So, let's all meet outside. OK?

Presenter: Before you hear some more information about the visit, you have some time to look at questions 14 and 15.

Presenter: Now listen and answer questions 14 and 15.

Teacher: Inside the museum, there are lots of things to see and do. But remember, there is no restaurant. So bring some sandwiches for lunch. We can sit and eat them together in the garden, which is very pretty. I know the museum very well and I can tell you all about the different exhibits. The museum doesn't have audio guides, so you are lucky to have me with you.

In the afternoon, we can watch a film about the history of the museum. There isn't a cinema there, but we can use a special education room where there is a video projector. And don't forget, bring some money. There are lots of lovely things in the gift shop – but it is expensive, so be careful!

Presenter: Before you hear some more information about the visit, you have some time to look at questions 16–20.

Presenter: Now listen and answer questions 16–20.

Teacher: OK. This is the programme for the visit. Each of the rooms is named after a colour, and each room has exhibits from a particular country. You can see very different things in the different rooms. For example, we begin in the Green Room. This has some wonderful paintings by Italian artists.

After that we go to the Blue Room. Here you can see the work of German artists, but the exhibits are all drawings this time. Some of them are absolutely beautiful.

The next room is the Red Room. Here we can see a fantastic collection of old English books. Some of them are really very old and you can't touch them. People wrote them by hand hundreds of years ago – before printing was invented.

The next room has something quite different. There is a large collection of ceramics – pots, plates and vases – all hand-painted by Japanese artists. The colours are wonderful. Ah yes – that's the Yellow Room. I nearly forgot to tell you the colour.

After that, we go to the Orange Room. There you can see some really old maps. This is a special exhibition. The maps are on loan from a Russian museum, and they're only here for four weeks.

My favourite exhibition is last of all and it's in the White Room. This time it's from Brazil. You know the carnival they have there every year? Well, in this exhibition, you can see some clothes that people wore for that big street party in the past. Some of them are amazing.

Presenter:	Now look at Section 3 on page 102 of your book. You will hear a married couple called Ben and Anna talking about their holidays. First, you have some time to look at questions 21 and 22.
Presenter:	Now listen and answer questions 21 and 22.
Ben:	Hi. My name's Ben.
Anna:	And I'm Anna. I'm his wife. Today we want to tell you about our holidays, don't we Ben?
Ben:	That's right. Anna and I love travelling. Every year, we go on holiday for a whole month. Not in July or August like a lot of people in this country – we like to go in September. Because we're not typical tourists, are we Anna?
Anna:	No, we're not. We plan our holidays very carefully and we do everything ourselves. We choose the places we want to visit. Then we book the accommodation and buy the tickets online. But we don't travel by car and we don't use public transport like trains and buses. We go everywhere by bicycle.
Ben:	It's great fun. We think everyone could enjoy holidays like ours. They are good exercise – and they're good for the environment.
Presenter:	Before you hear the rest of the conversation, you have some time to look at questions 23–30.
Presenter:	Now listen and answer questions 23–30.
Anna:	People always ask us how we organize our holidays. The answer is that we share things between us. For example, Ben really enjoys looking at maps and reading about places on the internet. So I let him do that, don't I Ben?
Ben:	That's right. I choose where we go and which route we take, because I want to see really interesting places and read all about them first. But when it comes to booking hotels and places to stay, I get bored. So Anna does that.
Anna:	Yes, I'm good at the practical details. But sometimes we decide things together. Like when we want to eat in a restaurant and we have to choose which one, we talk about it and decide together.
Ben:	Anna also says when we need a break from cycling. I love cycling and don't get tired, but Anna likes to have a break. She tells me when it's time to stop for a rest.
Anna:	And I like to check the phone for messages. When he's on a cycling holiday, Ben forgets everything at home. But I like to keep in touch with the family – so I answer any calls and texts we get.
Ben:	But Anna hates shopping. So when we need to buy food or other things, I go into the shops. Anna makes a list for me!
Anna:	And Ben hates taking photos, but I think it's important to have a memory of places. So I take lots of them on my phone. We also keep a blog. We write there about how far we have travelled and what we think of the places.
Ben:	I don't really like writing blogs, but it isn't fair if Anna does it all the time. So, we take turns to do that. I do it one day and Anna does it the next. It works well, doesn't it Anna?
Anna:	Yes, we're a great team! And we have fantastic holidays!
Presenter:	Now look at Section 4 on page 103 of your book. You will hear some information about lions. First, you have some time to look at questions 31–35.
Presenter:	Now listen and answer questions 31–35.
Woman:	Lions are fantastic animals. Everyone likes lions because they are strong and beautiful. You can see pictures of lions all over the world. Lions are members of the cat family and most of them live in Africa. There are also a few in Asia. Maybe in the past they also lived in Europe, but not these days.
	In the wild, lions usually live for about fifteen years. In zoos, they can live for twenty or thirty years, but this doesn't happen in their natural environment.
	Baby lions are called cubs. Sometimes only one cub is born, but usually there are as many as five born at the same time. Lions live in families and the parents take care of the baby lions until they are old enough to look after themselves.
	Lions spend a lot of time resting – twenty hours a day is not unusual. They spend the other hours looking for things to eat. Lions are hunters. They eat meat. The female lion often catches the animals the family eats – but she doesn't eat first. The male lion always starts the meal. The female and the cubs then eat what is left.
Presenter:	Before you hear the rest of the information, you have some time to look at questions 36–40.
Presenter:	Now listen and answer questions 36–40.
Woman:	An interesting fact about lions is that people have great respect for them. The lion is called the 'king of the jungle', and you see pictures and statues of lions everywhere. Sports clubs often use the name 'lions' because it's a good name for a team.
	For example, in the UK and Ireland, one of the most famous rugby teams is called 'the Lions'. And all over the world, there are other sports teams which use the animal in their names and as a symbol on their websites and T-shirts.
	In Malta, there is a soccer team called 'the Sannat Lions'. You hear the name 'lions' and think of the animal, which is strong and fast. It's a great name for all types of football teams. There are teams called 'the Lions' playing American football – like 'the Detroit Lions', and there is a team called 'the Lions' playing Australian Rules football.
	Another sports team that uses the name is 'the Highveld Lions', one of the most famous cricket teams in South Africa. That, at least, is a country where lions actually live!
	But there are no lions in cold countries. So, for 'the Lac St Louis Lions' ice hockey team in Canada, the lion is just a symbol. The same is true for 'the Dublin Lions' in Ireland. They play basketball. And there are volleyball and tennis clubs in many countries with the same name. They are all lions!
Presenter:	That is the end of the Listening test.

Answer key

Unit 1

1a (pages 4 and 5)

1
Bb Dd Ff Hh Jj Ll Nn Pp Rr Tt Vv Xx Zz

3
2 I   3 J   4 H   5 K   6 S   7 Q   8 W

4
2 P   3 N   4 Y   5 W

5a
1 door   2 chair   3 book   4 desk   5 window   6 board

5b
1 listen   2 look   3 read   4 repeat   5 say   6 write

6
I'm

7
1 I'm   2 I'm   3 you're

8
1 I   2 You, I   3 I, I   4 You

1b (pages 6 and 7)

1
2 Russia   3 Italy   4 Spain   5 Brazil
6 Canada   7 United States   8 Mexico   9 Egypt

2a
2 Egypt   3 Brazilian   4 Canadian   5 Italy
6 Mexico   7 Vietnamese

3
a nine   b three   c eight   d five   e two   f seven

4
2 He's Brazilian.
3 It's British.
4 She's Vietnamese.
5 It's Italian.
6 He's Egyptian.

5
1 is   2 He's   3 He's   4 is   5 is

6
1 I'm   2 I'm a   3 This is   4 She's a   5 She's
6 I'm from   7 It's

1c (page 8)

1
1 morning   2 afternoon   3 evening
4 night

2
1 b, a   2 c

3
1 Lisa   2 Nasser   3 Boris

4
Lisa – Mexico – Merida
Nasser – Egypt – London
Boris – Germany – New York

5
Lisa – 55 018 375
Nasser – 203 903 7529
Boris – 707 839 116

6
1 your   2 My   3 My   4 your   5 My

7
2 Joana is <u>from</u> Madrid.
4 This phone call is <u>from</u> Boris.
6 He's <u>from</u> South Africa.

1d (page 9)

1
1 pencil   2 computer   3 classroom   4 bag   5 notebook
6 pen   7 table   8 mobile phone

2
1 What's   2 late   3 understand   4 Open, page, Page
5 repeat   6 down   7 spell   8 home

1e (page 10)

1a
2 I'm from the United Kingdom.
3 Paula is from the United States.
4 Spain is in Europe.
5 Alex Robson is a doctor.
6 Hanoi is in Vietnam.

1b
a city – London
a country – Brazil
a language – French
a name – Robert Smith
a nationality – Canadian

2b
1 ?   2 .   3 .   4 ?   5 .   6 .   7 ?   8 ?

2c
1 What's your name? 5 My name's Chris Cavendish.
4 Can you spell that? 6 Yes. C–A–V–E–N–D–I–S–H.
7 How are you? 3 I'm fine.
8 What's your phone number? 2 It's 96 457 329.

3
First name – Greta
Surname – Lessard
Nationality – South African
Job – writer

Learning skills / Check! (page 11)

1
classroom objects: board, book, chair, computer, pen, pencil
nationalites: American, British, Egyptian, Italian, South
African, Spanish
numbers: eight, five, four, nine, one, seven, six, ten, three, two

3
1 student   2 photo   3 British   4 three   5 phone   6 seven

Unit 2

2a (pages 12 and 13)

1
2 lake   3 city   4 island   5 beach   6 mountain

2
1 Saturday   2 Wednesday   3 Tuesday   4 Friday
5 Thursday   6 Monday   7 Sunday

3
b

4
2 They're   3 They're   4 We're   5 We're   6 They're

5b

1 We're   2 They're   3 They're   4 We're   5 They're
6 We're

6

2 'm not   3 aren't   4 isn't   5 aren't   6 aren't

8

1 Wednesday   2 my   3 They're   4 aren't   5 holiday

2b (pages 14 and 15)

1

2 twenty-four   3 forty-seven   4 sixty-three   5 seventy-six
6 eighty-one

2

Berlin – 33°C
Paris – 30°C
Rio de Janeiro – 37°C
Sydney – 18°C
Toronto – 29°C

3

2 twenty-six   3 twenty-one   4 twenty-two   5 thirty-six
6 seventeen

4

2 No, it isn't.   3 No, it isn't.   4 Yes, it is.   5 Yes, it is.
6 No, it isn't.

5

2 ✓   3 ?   4 ?   5 ✓   6 ?   7 ✓   8 ?

6

2 Are John and Jane in Rome?
3 She's on the beach.
4 Paul and Meera are in Santiago.
5 Is your name Andy?
6 You're OK.
7 Is it cold in London today?
8 They're tourists.

2c (page 16)

1

1 black   2 orange   3 brown   4 red   5 blue   6 green
7 white   8 yellow   9 pink

2

1 a   2 a   3 an   4 a   5 an

3

1 What's this colour <u>in</u> English?
2 Are you <u>in</u> a hotel?
3 Are they <u>in</u> Tokyo?
1 b   2 a   3 c

4

1 cold   2 white   3 blue   4 grey   5 hotel   6 friend

5

1 buses   2 tents   3 cars   4 cities   5 offices   6 photos

6

1 friends   2 island   3 countries   4 Mountains   5 hotel
6 beaches

2d (page 17)

1

1 a, d   2 b, e   3 c, f

2

1 Where   2 What   3 Is   4 What
1 Belfast
2 27 Front Street
3 mross@gmail.com
4 LE61 DGM

3

Address – 17 North Street
Email address – julia21@gmail.com
Phone number – 0794 276 809

5

email – 2   holiday – 3   hotel – 2   island – 2   lake – 1
mountain – 2   number – 2   student – 2   teacher – 2
telephone – 3   tourist – 2

2e (page 18)

1a

1 10 Downing Street London – c
2 221b Baker Street London – d
3 350 Fifth Avenue New York – a
4 1600 Pennsylvania Avenue Washington – b

1b

Ness Hotel
Loch Road
Inverness
IV4 2HF

1c

First name – David
Surname – Smith
Address – 64 Mill Road
City – Manchester
Postcode – M17 6RT
Country – UK

2

Title – Mrs
First name – Diana
Surname – Black
Address – 26 Hill Street
City – London
Postcode – SW18 3ND
Country – UK
Email address – d.black@gmail.com

Learning skills / Check! (page 19)

1

1 b   2 c   3 a   4 d

5

Brown, green and red are colours.
Cuba, Fiji and Hawaii are islands.
Loch Ness and Titicaca are lakes.
Cape Town, Moscow and Paris are cities.

Unit 3

3a (pages 20 and 21)

1

1 brother   2 sister   3 mother   4 father

2

1 daughter   2 sons   3 parents

3

2 brother, sister   3 husband, wife   4 mother, daughter

4

1 Her, Her   2 Our, Its   3 His   4 Their, Their, their
5 Her, her   6 His, His

5

1 What   2 Who   3 When   4 How   5 Where

3b (pages 22 and 23)

1

1 eyes   2 old   3 tall   4 young   5 hair   6 short

2
2 Liam is my brother's friend.
3 Who's Anne's teacher?
4 What's Moira's phone number?
5 Is this Jerry's car?
6 Are you Liam's best friend?
7 What's David's surname?

3
2 Luigi is Kate's husband.
3 Stan's hair is red.
4 Jane's dad isn't old.
5 Carola and Marin are Bill's best friends.
6 Rosa's sister is tall.
7 Ed's surname is Smith.

4
2 It's Eva's bag.
3 They're Ahmed's pencils.
4 It's Felipe's computer.
5 They're Claude's pens.
6 It's Enzo's phone.

5
1 is   2 P   3 P   4 is   5 is   6 P

7
1 are you
2 is your husband
3 are your parents
4 is your daughter

8
1 twenty-nine
2 twenty-eight
3 father: sixty-five; mother: fifty-nine
4 seven

9
2 Kate's husband   3 Kate's daughter   4 Kate's mother

10a
1 Where are your parents from?
2 What's your mother's name?
3 What's your father's job?
4 What's your friend's phone number?
5 Where's your teacher from?
6 Who are your friends in your English class?

3c (page 24)

1
1 March   2 May   3 October   4 September

2
1 April, June, September, November
2 January, March, May, July, August, October, December

4
1 children – I   2 countries – R   3 families – R   4 men – I
5 people – I   6 women – I

5
1 British   2 countries   3 young   4 age   5 five   6 old

6
1 Look at the photo on page 23.
2 My friends are on holiday in London.
3 Is your English class on Monday?
4 In this photo, we're on a beach in Thailand.
5 The number is on the key.
6 Bye. See you on Friday!

3d (page 25)

1
1 a wedding   2 a new year   3 a new baby
4 a birthday

2
1 b   2 d   3 a   4 c

4
1 c a b   2 b c a

3e (page 26)

1
1 ✓   2 ✓   3 ✓   4 ✗   5 ✓   6 ✗

2
1 are not   2 he is   3 I am   4 is not   5 they are   6 we are
7 what is   8 when is   9 who is   10 you are

3
1 What's his address?
2 It isn't their car.
4 They're students.
6 What's your sister's name?

4
To Sandra
Happy Birthday!
Best wishes from Laura and George

5
To Martina and Jeff
Congratulations on your new son!
Love from Alex

Learning skills / Check! (page 27)

1
1 classmates   2 old   3 eyes   4 son   5 present   6 men

3
1 artist   2 actress   3 athlete   4 singer

4
1 women   2 brothers   3 family   4 wedding   5 celebration
6 people

5
1 wedding   2 family   3 women   4 brothers
5 celebration   6 person

Unit 4

4a (pages 28 and 29)

1
1 bank   2 café   3 park   4 cinema   5 market   6 museum
7 car park   8 bus station   9 train station
10 information centre

2
1 park   2 cinema   3 museum   4 car park

3a
1 k   2 k   3 s   4 s   5 s   6 k

4
1 Kent Street   2 Norfolk Street   3 Kent Street
4 Norfolk Street

5
1 Express Café – b
2 bus station – d
3 market – c
4 bank – a

6
2 The bus station is in Norfolk Street
3 The Express Café is next to the museum.
4 The market is near the Express Café.
5 The information centre is next to the bank.
6 The cinema is opposite the bank.

7a
1 The cinema is next to the bus station.
2 The museum is in Norfolk Street.
3 The market is near the bus station.
4 The cinema is opposite the café.

7b
1 T   2 F   3 F   4 F

4b (pages 30 and 31)

1
1 this, these   2 that, those

2b
1 The bank is open today.
2 This is a map of London.
3 That's the famous river.
4 See you there next time!
5 They're on holiday in Rome.
6 What are these timetables?

3
2 guidebook   3 timetable   4 Excuse me   5 map
6 open   7 train

4
1 The Old Market   2 Main Street, Alston   3 no

5
1 What is this building?
2 Where are we?
3 When is the market open?
4 Why is this building famous?

6
a street

7
a Where is that?
b When is it open?
c Is it open today?
d Is it on the map?
e What is the name of this street?

8
1 e What is / What's the name of this street?
2 a Where is / Where's that?
3 d Is it on the map?
4 c Is it open today?
5 b When is / When's it open?

4c (page 32)

1
2 It's ten fifteen.
3 It's twelve thirty.
4 It's five twenty.
5 It's six ten.
6 It's eight forty-five.

2
2 It's eleven thirty.
3 It's nine fifteen.
4 It's two forty-five.
5 It's four o'clock.
6 It's ten twenty.

3
1 nine in the morning, eight in the evening
2 Monday, Friday, nine o'clock, three thirty
3 five in the evening, midnight
4 Tuesday

4
1 in   2 at   3 at   4 at   5 in

5
1 Addis Ababa   2 London   3 no   4 East Africa Time,
traditional Ethiopian time

6
b traditional Ethiopian time   c East Africa Time

4d (page 33)

1
1 coffee   2 tea   3 fruit juice   4 mineral water   5 cake
6 sandwich   7 salad

2
1 b   2 a   3 c   4 b   5 a   6 c   7 a   8 b

4e (page 34)

1
2 Our hotel is near the old city and the sea.
3 The Grand Bazaar is old and famous.
4 The coffee and the food are great.
5 The people are nice and friendly.
6 The Topkapi Palace museum and the Hagia Sophia
   museum are great.

2
1 b   2 a   3 f   4 c   5 d   6 e
1 It's hot and sunny here.
2 The museum is closed on Sunday and Monday.
3 The park and (the) station are in Cambridge Street.
4 The town is beautiful and its centre is famous.
5 The coffee and (the) cakes are great.
6 The train station is old and beautiful.

3
1 Hello   2 in   3 near   4 and   5 is   6 here   7 great   8 you

Learning skills / Check! (page 35)

2
1 here   2 this   3 name   4 near   5 open   6 time
7 please   8 help

V	E	Y	P	L	E	A	S	E	E
O	T	L	E	N	E	B	X	Q	Y
N	H	Q	B	T	P	C	O	G	T
A	I	W	I	H	L	V	P	W	N
M	S	H	E	L	P	M	E	G	E
E	O	R	W	J	S	K	N	P	A
W	O	Y	I	J	D	O	S	L	R
B	I	U	O	Q	H	E	R	E	V
Y	T	I	M	E	V	L	T	A	I
O	A	Z	E	O	C	S	R	I	A

Unit 5

5a (pages 36 and 37)

1
1 can   2 can't   3 can't   4 can   5 can   6 can

2b
1 can   2 can't   3 can't   4 can   5 can   6 can't

3
1 play   2 drive   3 play   4 sing   5 cook   6 ride
7 swim   8 speak

4
2 Can you drive a car?

3 Can your father play table tennis?
4 Can your sister sing?
5 Can your mother cook?
6 Can you ride a bike?
7 Can your brother swim?
8 Can your friends speak English?

5
1 I can't.   2 I can.   3 he can't.   4 she can't.   5 she can.
6 I can.   7 he can't.   8 they can.

5b (pages 38 and 39)

1
1 a camera   2 a cat   3 a football   4 glasses   5 a guitar
6 a motorbike   7 photos   8 a watch

2
1 F   2 T   3 T   4 F

3
2 Alvaro has a guitar and photos.
3 Linzi and Jay have a motorbike and a watch.
4 Boris has a guitar and a watch.
5 Simona has photos and a camera.
6 John and Mimi have a watch and a camera.

4
1 have   2 has   3 have   4 has   5 have   6 has

6
Adjective: beautiful, expensive, famous, fantastic, friendly, good, great, interesting, new, nice, old, small, young
Noun: battery, family, invention, office, photo, robot, supermarket

7
2 expensive   3 young   4 big   5 young   6 friendly

8
1 a   2 b   3 a   4 b   5 b

5c (page 40)

1
c

2
1 T   2 T   3 F   4 T   5 F

3
1 has   2 big   3 small   4 isn't   5 can't   6 poor

4
1 battery   2 camera   3 memory stick   4 screen   5 webcam
6 headphones   7 tablet   8 laptop

5
2 These are grey glasses.
3 You have a white car.
4 My friend has a new tablet.
5 My phone has great apps.
6 I have a small bag.

6
1 What's the name of this building?
2 What's the capital of France?
3 Is that a map of the city centre?
4 This is a photo of my family.
5 I'm from the United States of America.

5d (page 41)

1
2 £   3 $ 4 R$ 5 AED   6 ¥

2
1 £30.00   2 £14.50   3 £16.60   4 £17.85   5 £80.20   6 £90.99

4
1 nineteen euros   2 ninety-five euros   3 yes

5
1 Can I help you?
2 How much are these speakers?
3 And how much is this alarm clock?
4 Can I pay with euros?
5 Here you are.

5e (page 42)

1a
1 good, but   2 swim, but   3 great and   4 cook and
5 old, but   6 a good screen and

1b
2 My computer is new, but it is very slow.
3 This phone is very basic, but it is cheap.
4 This shop is big, but it isn't very good.
5 I can ride a motorbike, but I can't drive a car.
6 She can speak Russian, but she can't write in Russian.

2
phone, laptop, computer

3
1 d   2 c   3 a   4 b

4
Example answer:
Hi Pascal
Laptops are cheap, but you can't carry a laptop in your pocket. New phones are expensive, but Skype is cheap. Good luck in your new job!
Mike

Learning skills / Check! (page 43)

1
1 piano   2 swim   3 alarm clock

4
1 robot   2 piano   3 bike   4 college   5 euro   6 tennis

5
tablet

Unit 6

6a (pages 44 and 45)

1
1 tennis   2 basketball   3 swimming   4 running   5 cycling

2
2 We don't like football.
3 We don't like cycling.
4 We like tennis.
5 We don't like basketball.
6 We like swimming.

3
2 Do they like football? No, they don't.
3 Do they like cycling? No, they don't.
4 Do they like tennis? Yes, they do.
5 Do they like basketball? No, they don't.
6 Do they like swimming? Yes, they do.

6
a five hundred   b nine million   c seven thousand
d twenty-five million   e thirteen thousand
f eighty-eight thousand   g ten million

7
1 three hundred   2 200 / two hundred
3 10,000 / ten thousand   4 65,000,000 / sixty-five million
5 210,000,000 / two hundred and ten million

8a
1 b   2 e   3 a   4 c   5 d

8b
1 What time is it?
2 How much is it?
3 What day is it?
4 Is it hot today?
5 Do you like football?

6b (pages 46 and 47)

1
1 books   2 swimming   3 action films   4 music
5 TV shows   6 birds

2
1 birds   2 TV shows   3 action films   4 music
5 swimming   6 books

3
1 jazz   2 reality shows   3 Sherlock Holmes

4
☺ reality shows, comedies, detective stories
☹ animals, wildlife shows, action films, sports

5
2 He likes reality shows.
3 He likes comedies.
4 He likes detective stories.
5 He doesn't like animals.
6 He doesn't like wildlife shows.
7 He doesn't like action films.
8 He doesn't like sports.

6
2 Andrew's friend doesn't like jazz.
3 Does Emile like scuba diving?
4 Emile doesn't like novels.
5 Frances doesn't like pop music.
6 Does Frances like tennis?

8b
1 a lot   2 very much

8c
1 Andrew likes jazz a lot.
2 He doesn't like pop music very much.
3 I don't like tea very much.
4 We like sports a lot.
5 My friend doesn't like TV very much.
6 My friends like films a lot.

6c (page 48)

1
cheese, chocolate, eggs, fish, fruit, meat, pasta, rice, salad, vegetables

2
1 international   2 four   3 the United Kingdom / Great Britain

3
c

4
1 c   2 c   3 a

5
1 it   2 him   3 them   4 her   5 you   6 me

6d (page 49)

1
1 ☹   2 ☺   3 ☺   4 ☹

2
1 horrible   2 great   3 fantastic   4 boring

5
1 play   2 don't like   3 like   4 watch   5 love
6 have   7 don't like

6e (page 50)

1a
2 A: This film is boring!
2 B: Oh! I think it's very good.
3 B: Yes, I do. She's fantastic!

1b
2 No, I can't come tonight.
3 Do you like tennis? I have two tickets.
4 Yes, we love Italian food!
5 Let's go to the cinema.
6 That's a great idea! I love pizza!

1c
2 Can you send me a message?
3 Do they like meat?
4 She doesn't like fish very much.
5 What time can you come?
6 They have an English class at 5.30.

2
1 It   2 it   3 They   4 them   5 They   6 We

3
Example answers:
1 Yes, let's meet at the café in the afternoon. What time?
2 I'm sorry. I don't like basketball very much.
3 I'm not at home, but I have my mobile with me. You can phone me now.
4 I love Tom Cruise, but I have all his films on DVD.

Learning skills / Check! (page 51)

1
You can find out all this information from a dictionary.

3
1 women   2 no – it's *bicycle*   3 a special day or celebration   4 /təˈnaɪt/   5 horrible   6 an adjective

5
basketball, cheese, eggs, football, pasta, salad, tennis, vegetables

B	I	H	T	F	U	I	F	O	J	X
L	C	H	E	E	S	E	F	O	Y	P
O	E	P	N	Q	E	P	O	Q	Q	E
E	Y	A	N	A	R	O	O	D	S	K
E	T	P	I	W	L	W	T	I	A	A
T	B	A	S	K	E	T	B	A	L	L
I	O	S	A	U	G	A	A	A	A	R
V	I	T	R	I	G	S	L	X	D	I
S	S	A	M	D	S	G	L	E	E	F
D	E	T	N	F	Z	H	I	B	T	L
V	E	G	E	T	A	B	L	E	S	W

Unit 7

7a (pages 52 and 53)

1
a autumn   b spring   c summer   d winter

2
1 d   2 b   3 c   4 a

3
1 breakfast   2 lunch   3 dinner   4 work   5 bed

4
get up – 6.30
start work – 7.00
have lunch – 11.30
finish work – ✓
go to bed – ✓

5
3 They don't start work at half past seven.
   They start work at seven o'clock.
4 They don't have lunch at eleven o'clock.
   They have lunch at one o'clock.
5 They don't finish work at half past five.
   They finish work at half past three.
6 They don't go to bed at eleven o'clock.
   They go to bed at ten o'clock.

7
1 at   2 on   3 at   4 at   5 in   6 on

7b (pages 54 and 55)

1
1 climbing   2 cooking   3 dancing   4 painting   5 shopping
6 singing

2
1 cooking, painting, singing, dancing
2 shopping
3 climbing, painting

3
1 T   2 T   3 F

4
1 c   2 e   3 d   4 b   5 a

5
2 Do you live in Zanzibar?
3 Do you make videos?
4 Do you have a YouTube cannel?
5 Do you like the culture of Zanzibar?
6 Do you enjoy the Zanzibar International Film Festival?

6
1 Do you understand Kiswahili?
2 Do your friends make videos?
3 Do we have an internet connection?
4 Do your friends go to festivals?
5 Do they enjoy singing?
6 Do you listen to music?

7
1 Yes, I do. *or* No, I don't.
2 Yes, they do. *or* No, they don't.
3 Yes, you do. *or* No, you don't.
4 Yes, they do. *or* No, they don't.
5 Yes, they do. *or* No, they don't.
6 Yes, I do. *or* No, I don't.

7c (page 56)

1
1 cloudy   2 rainy   3 snowy   4 sunny   5 windy

2
2 eat   3 watch   4 stay   5 read   6 cook   7 play   8 take

3
You hear all the activities except 4.
interview 1: meet my friends at the park, eat lunch outside,
don't watch TV
interview 2: read books a lot, cook with my sister
interview 3: don't play golf, take a lot of photos

4
1 What   2 When   3 Where   4 Who   5 Why

5
1 outside   2 beach   3/4 cycling/swimming   5 university

7d (page 57)

1
5 ~~Is it~~   6 ~~It's~~   7 ~~It's~~

2
1 c   2 g   3 a   4 f   5 d   6 e   7 b

3a
1 feel   2 like   3 magazine   4 bed   5 tea   6 dictionary

7e (page 58)

1
a cycling   b Pacific Technical College   c married
d teacher   e cycling   f Saturdays   g two children
h two bikes

2
1 b, d   2 c, g   3 a, e, f, h

3
1
d I'm a teacher.
b I work at Pacific Technical College.

2
c I'm married.
g I have two children – a boy and a girl.

3
a I like cycling.
h I have two bikes.
e We go cycling in the mountains.
f We meet on Saturdays.

4
Example answers:
1 I speak Japanese.
2 Today is Tuesday.
3 This month is June.
4 My favourite season is autumn.
5 I study at the Escola Oficial d'Idiomes.

Learning skills / Check! (page 59)

3
1 Indian   2 winter   3 dhow   4 autumn   5 singing
6 Holi   7 Canada   8 islands

4
1 HOLINDIAN   2 ISLANDSINGING
3 CANADAUTUMN   4 DHOWINTER

Unit 8

8a (pages 60 and 61)

1
2 in   3 in   4 with   5 in   6 with   7 in   8 in

3
1 T   2 F   3 F

4

1 writes   2 doesn't like   3 gets up   4 doesn't drive
5 doesn't know

5

2 enjoys   3 doesn't sell   4 doesn't write   5 doesn't watch
6 walks

6a

1 works   2 gets up   3 start   4 watch   5 finishes   6 goes

7

1 doctor   2 waiter   3 photographer   4 taxi driver
5 receptionist   6 shop assistant

8a

1 Pauline checks papers.
2 Amelia doesn't use a computer.
3 Lisa answers questions and doesn't help people.
4 Kris doesn't work alone.
5 Jamal doesn't work in an office.
6 Bill sells snacks.

8b

1 Pauline doesn't check papers.
2 Amelia uses a computer.
3 Lisa doesn't answer questions and doesn't help people.
4 Kris works alone.
5 Jamal works in an office.
6 Bill doesn't sell snacks.

8b (pages 62 and 63)

1

1 teacher   2 board   3 student   4 pencil   5 book   6 pen
classroom

2

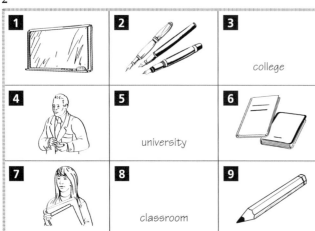

3

2 Does Tarik live in the capital?
3 Does Zahid like his school?
4 Does the school open every day?
5 Does Majed study English?
6 Does Tarik have classes in English?

5

1 No, he doesn't.
2 No, he doesn't.
3 Yes, he does.
4 No, it doesn't.
5 Yes, he does.
6 No, he doesn't.

6

1 do (you) do   2 works   3 Does (your wife) do
4 doesn't   5 Do (you) enjoy   6 do   7 has   8 helps
9 gives

7

2 the teacher   3 the board   4 a book   5 a classmate
6 a notebook   7 a pen

8c (page 64)

1

scientists in a 'sleep laboratory'

2

1 a   2 c   3 e   4 b   5 d

3

1 I usually sleep for eight hours.
2 Scientists often study people.
3 Police officers sometimes work twelve hours.
4 I never work at home.
5 Shop assistants always talk to customers. or Customers always talk to shop assistants.

4

1 She goes to work <u>every</u> day.
2 Do you change your routine <u>every</u> week?
3 We meet <u>every</u> month.
4 I talk to my mother <u>every</u> evening.
5 Does he work <u>every</u> night?
6 We go to the beach <u>every</u> Sunday in summer.

8d (page 65)

1

1 e   2 d   3 a   4 e   5 d   6 c   7 b

4a

calls – is, colours – is, drives – is, experiments – this,
has – is, journalists – this, laboratories – is, nurse – this,
wakes – this, writes – this

8e (page 66)

1a

1 boss   2 businessman   3 call   4 college   5 different
6 difficult   7 dinner   8 engineer   9 finish   10 meeting
11 midday   12 sleep   13 summer   14 tourist   15 usually
16 week
The words *finish* and *tourist* don't have double letters.

1b

1 engineer   2 college   3 dinner   4 usually

2a

1 time   2 place

2b

3 night   4 the morning   5 university   6 Italy

3

1 a   2 d   3 g   4 c   5 e   6 b   7 f

4

boss, difficult, midday, usually, week

5

Example answer:
Hi Craig
Yes, I'm in Italy. I have a new job too. I work in a call centre.
It's boring, but it isn't difficult.
I finish work at eight o'clock. Let's talk at nine o'clock.
Oscar

Learning skills / Check! (page 67)

2

1 breakfast   2 receptionist   3 cats   4 lunch   5 exercise
6 dinner   7 film   8 bed

Unit 9

9a (pages 68 and 69)

1
1 a hat 2 a scarf 3 a jacket 4 a jumper 5 a pair of jeans

2
1 a T-shirt 2 a pair of boots 3 a shirt
4 a coat 5 a pair of trousers 6 a pair of shoes

3
pyramids – Mexico
a castle – Edinburgh
shops – Tokyo
beaches – Indonesia
old buildings – Russia
a prison – South Africa

4
1 365 2 yes 3 Indonesia 4 yes

5
1 There are 2 There's 3 There are 4 There are
5 There are 6 There's

8
1 There are four shirts in my suitcase.
2 They're red and white.
3 There are two pairs of trousers.
4 They're old.
5 There are three jumpers.
6 They're new.

9b (pages 70 and 71)

1
1 table 2 lamp 3 bed 4 chair 5 desk 6 TV
7 fridge 8 bath 9 wardrobe
not in the picture: armchair, shower, sofa

2
Executive

3
2 Is there a DVD player in the Club rooms?
3 Are there magazines in the Executive rooms?
4 Is there a basket of fruit in the Superior rooms?
5 Are there drinks in the Executive rooms?
6 Is there a fridge in the Superior rooms?

4
2 Yes, there is. 3 No, there aren't. 4 No, there isn't.
5 No, there aren't. 6 Yes, there is.

5
2 There aren't any armchairs in the Executive rooms.
3 There isn't a DVD player in the Superior rooms.
4 There isn't a basket of fruit in the Executive rooms.
5 There isn't a safe in the Executive rooms.
6 There aren't any magazines in the Superior rooms.

6
1 Are there any 2 there are 3 there's 4 Is there
5 there isn't 6 there's 7 there isn't 8 Is there 9 there is
10 there aren't any

7a
A: Let's go to Loch Ness for New Year.
A: Yes, there are. There are flights from Monday to Friday.
A: Yes. It's popular in winter – from December to February
    there are lots of flights.
A: And there's a bus from the airport to the hotel.

7b
1 T 2 T

9c (page 72)

1
1 the North Island 2 by car 3 740 kilometres
4 Auckland – Wellington 5 bed and breakfast places

2
1 T 2 T 3 F 4 T 5 T

3
1 b 2 a 3 d 4 c 5 f 6 e

4
1 Can I take two suitcases on the plane?
2 Can I take photos in the plane?
3 Can I take a bus to the airport?

5
1 Start 2 Don't drive 3 Don't stay 4 Visit 5 Go

9d (page 73)

1
1 restaurant 2 wi-fi 3 swimming pool 4 car park
5 gift shop 6 café

2
1 a 2 b 3 c 4 c

3
1 Certainly. 2 Here you are. 3 Yes, of course.
4 That's no problem.

9e (page 74)

1a
2 You can swim every day because the beach is next to the
  hotel.
3 Stay in bed and breakfasts because they're cheap and
  friendly.
4 Don't go in winter because it's very cold.
5 There are a lot of hotels because it's a popular place.
6 Don't take a bus because they aren't comfortable.

1b
1 d 2 c 3 a 4 b 5 e

2
1 b 2 c 3 d 4 a

3
Example answer:
Legoland is a great place for families. It's near London.
There are a lot of attractions. Don't go in August because
there are a lot of people at that time. There's a hotel in the
park. Don't miss the children's train because it's great for
young children.

Learning skills / check! (page 75)

1
take a photo, take a suitcase
book a hotel, book online
travel by bus, travel to Africa

2
Example answers:
go: to school/work, home, to the beach, to bed, to a class,
to Africa, into the forest, swimming, for walks, out,
on holiday; temperatures go up
have: classes, a meeting, teachers, children, a camera,
a mineral water, breakfast/lunch

3
1 Peru 2 Russia 3 636 kilometres
4 the Trans-Siberian railway 5 Lisbon 6 a pyramid
7 Wellington 8 yes

4

1 table   2 beds   3 fridge   4 sofa   5 bath

5

wardrobe

Unit 10

10a (pages 76 and 77)

1

2 1991   3 1836   4 2005   5 1492   6 1770

2

2 two thousand   3 eighteen seventy-five
4 two thousand and fifteen   5 seventeen fifty
6 two thousand and eight

3

2 4th   3 12th   4 18th   5 22nd   6 31st

5

b second   c third   d fourth   e fifth   f tenth   g eleventh
h twelfth   i thirteenth   j twenty-first

6

1 Marie Skłodowska Curie   2 scientist
3 woman winner of a Nobel Prize and first woman
professor at the University of Paris
4 7th November 1867   5 Poland   6 French
7 scientist   8 France

7

1 October   2 scientist   3 Sweden   4 parents   5 engineer
6 brothers   7 rich

8

1 was   2 were   3 was   4 were   5 was   6 was

9

2 He was an engineer and inventor.
3 He was the inventor of television.
4 His parents were from Scotland.
5 He was born in Scotland.
6 His children were born in England.

11a

1 Irene Curie was born on 12th September 1897.
2 Eve Curie was born in 1904.
3 John Logie Baird was born in 1888.
4 Sally Ride was born on 26th May 1951.
5 Alfred Nobel was born on 21st October 1833.
6 Mao Zedong was born in 1893.

11b

1 years   2 dates

12a

there was, there were

12b

1 was   2 were   3 were   4 were   5 were   6 was

10b (pages 78 and 79)

1

1 famous   2 interesting   3 good   4 great   5 funny

2

1 boring   2 terrible   3 bad   4 unhappy

3

1 F   2 T   3 F   4 T   5 F   6 F

4

2 His parents weren't rich.
3 His first job wasn't in a film.
4 His first film roles weren't big.
5 He wasn't a happy child.

5

Example answers:
2 My parents weren't actors.
3 My grandparents weren't famous.
4 My brother wasn't a student in London.
5 I wasn't in a TV show in 1997.

6

1 Was your school big?
2 Were you good at science?
3 Were the teachers friendly?
4 Were the lessons interesting?
5 Was your best friend in your class?
6 Were your classmates nice?

7

2 No, I wasn't.
3 No, they weren't.
4 Yes, they were.
5 Yes, she was.
6 Yes, they were.

10c (page 80)

1

1 an Aztec leader
2 Mexico
3 Moctezuma – or Montezuma

2

1 F   2 T   3 T   4 T

3

1 lived   2 died   3 lived   4 was born   5 died
6 was born, lived

4a

1 Where were your parents from?
2 When was your father born?
3 What was your grandmother's name?
4 Who was your best friend at school?

5

1 first   2 last   3 first   4 first   5 last   6 last   7 first   8 last

10d (page 81)

1

1 e   2 d   3 c   4 a   5 b   6 f

2

b I was at home.
c I was in traffic.
d I was on the phone.
e I wasn't well.
f I was busy.

3

1 b   2 d   3 a   4 e   5 g   6 c   7 f

10e (page 82)

1

1 A   2 A   3 S   4 A

2

1 Dear / Hi
2 All the best / Love
3 Dear
4 Best wishes / Best regards
5 Dear
6 All the best / Best wishes / Best regards
7 Hi
8 Love

3
1 d   2 a   3 b   4 c

4
Example answers:
1 Hi Ali
  I'm very sorry, but I don't know your new phone number.
  Can you send it to me?
  All the best
  Jim
2 Dear Ms Brown
  I'm very sorry, but I can't come to the conference in June.
  June is a very busy time in the office.
  Best regards
  Sandra Cross
3 Dear Mr Panjabi
  I apologize for the delay in my reply to your email. Here
  is the information.
  Best regards
  Luisa Torres
4 Hi Gina
  I'm sorry you aren't well. I hope to see you soon.
  Love
  Tomas

Learning skills / Check! (page 83)

1
1 d   2 a   3 b   4 g   5 e   6 f   7 i   8 j   9 h   10 c

4
1 Apache   2 Russia   3 Japanese   4 Portugal   5 South
6 Norway   7 Maya

5
history

Unit 11

11a (pages 84 and 85)

1
2 h   3 e   4 a   5 d   6 f   7 b   8 g

2
2 finished – R   3 went – I   4 found – I   5 called – R
6 took – I

3
1 I took a bus to town.
2 I went to work.
3 We had a bad evening.
4 A customer found a snail in his food.
the waiter

4
1 called   2 died   3 discovered   4 finished   5 killed
6 lived   7 started   8 studied   9 walked

5
1 lived   2 started   3 died   4 studied   5 walked
6 finished

7
1 found *or* discovered   2 were   3 was   4 had   5 died
6 studied   7 found *or* discovered   8 lived

11b (pages 86 and 87)

1
1 Oxford
2 he was an actor and a TV writer from 1965 to 1980
3 1980
4 1969
5 thirty years (three books of his diaries – each book about a
  period of ten years in his life)

2
2 studied   3 made   4 found   5 changed   6 went
7 wrote   8 followed   9 started   10 published
11 prepared   12 remembered

3
2 He didn't make a film in 1980.
  He made a TV show in 1980.
3 He didn't write *Around the world in 80 days*.
  Jules Verne wrote *Around the world in 80 days*.
4 He didn't travel to the South Pole in 1999.
  He travelled to the South Pole in 1991.
5 He didn't go around the Pacific Ocean in two months.
  He went around the Pacific Ocean in ten months.
6 He didn't walk across the Sahara Desert in 2005.
  He walked across the Sahara Desert in 2002.

4
2 Did your wife go on your trips?
3 Did you drive to the South Pole?
4 Did you meet interesting people?
5 Did your children read your diaries?
6 Did you write a book last year?

6
2 she didn't   3 I didn't   4 I did   5 they did   6 I did

7
1 was   2 lived   3 went   4 left   5 studied   6 started
7 met   8 Michelle Obama

11c (page 88)

1
1 two men – Borge Ousland and Mike Horn
2 the North Pole   3 sledges   4 a polar bear

2
2 e   3 c   4 a   5 d   6 f

3
1 Who did Borge Ousland travel with?
2 When did they go to the North Pole?
3 What did the polar bear eat?
4 Where did Mike Horn fall?
5 Why did Mike Horn fall?
6 Why did Borge Ousland start a fire?

4
1 Mike Horn   2 in 2006   3 their boat   4 into the sea
5 because the ice broke   6 to dry Horn's clothes

5
1 the North Pole   2 email   3 bread   4 presents   5 bus
6 home

11d (page 89)

1
conversation 1: 2 c   3 e   4 b   5 d   6 f
conversation 2: 1 b   2 e   3 d   4 c   5 a   6 f
conversation 3: 1 b   2 f   3 c   4 e   5 d   6 a

3
2 h   3 f   4 g   5 d   6 c   7 a   8 e

11e (page 90)

2
1 When I was five, my brother was born.
2 When I was at school, I learned a lot of English.
3 When I was at secondary school, I played football and
  basketball.
4 When my parents were children, they lived in Mexico.
5 When I was a child, my favourite food was pizza.

3

Example answers:

a

When I was ten, my best friend was Denise Lagarde. My hobbies were swimming and running. I liked pizza – it was my favourite food. On TV, I liked sports shows because I liked swimming and running. My parents worked in a supermarket. We lived in a small town near the capital city. I lived with my mum, dad and my brother. My friend Gina was my neighbour. We went to Gates School. I liked maths and my favourite teacher was the maths teacher, Mrs Jones. I was in the chess club at school.

b

When I was thirteen, my best friends were Billy, Andrew and Sam. My hobbies were football and horses. My favourite food was fish and chips. On TV, I liked animal shows because I liked animals. We lived on a farm and my parents worked on the farm. I lived with my mum, dad and grandfather. I went to the Allen Academy. I liked science and my favourite teacher was the science teacher, Mrs Watson. I wasn't in any clubs at school.

Learning skills / Check! (page 91)

1

cut – cut, do – did, eat – ate, fall – fell, get – got, go – went, have – had, hide – hid, know – knew, leave – left, meet – met, see – saw, take – took, throw – threw

3

1 Ötzi   2 Italy   3 knife   4 New Orleans   5 Madagascar
6 very sharp   7 animal   8 Jules Verne   9 Sahara
10 polar bear

Unit 12

12a (pages 92 and 93)

1

1 bathroom   2 bedroom   3 kitchen   4 dining room
5 living room

2

2 I eat lunch in the dining room / kitchen / living room.
3 I cook in the kitchen.
4 I sleep in my / the bedroom.
5 I have a bath in the bathroom.

3

1 Kolkata, India
2 in the living room of the grandfather's house   3 eight

4

1 The man is sitting on a chair.
2 The children are sitting on the floor.
3 The boy is looking at the camera.
4 The girl is standing near a small table.
    She is wearing a dress.

6

2 Are the children watching TV?
  No, they aren't.
3 Is the man reading a book?
  No, he isn't.
4 Are the children sitting?
  Yes, they are.
5 Is the girl making tea?
  No, she isn't.
6 Are the boys wearing shorts?
  Yes, they are.

7

1 Are they making lunch?
2 He isn't reading the newspaper.
3 You're watching TV.
4 We're washing the car.
5 Are you eating?
6 She isn't sitting on the floor.

8

1 What are you doing?
2 I'm watching TV.
3 What are you watching?
4 Are you watching TV?
5 No, I'm not.
6 We're playing a video game.
7 I'm coming to your house.
8 I'm leaving the house right now.

12b (pages 94 and 95)

1

1 have   2 visit   3 play   4 go out   5 go   6 meet
7 get up   8 go   9 read   10 go   11 make   12 read

2

2 Adela and Naomi are meeting friends on Saturday evening.
3 Mike is visiting his family this weekend.
4 Rowan is reading the newspaper.
5 Leila is going out for a meal with colleagues tomorrow.
6 Joe and Sue are going shopping with their children on Saturday morning.

3

2 on Saturday evening   3 this weekend   4 now
5 tomorrow   6 on Saturday morning

4

1 working   2 taking the train to Edinburgh
3 going to a concert   4 meeting friends   5 coming back from Edinburgh   6 going shopping   7 having

5

1 tomorrow evening   2 tomorrow   3 next year
4 on Monday

6

2 Rosa is taking the train to Edinburgh on Saturday morning.
3 She's going to a concert on Saturday evening.
4 She's meeting friends on Sunday.
5 She's coming back from Edinburgh on Monday evening.
6 Carla is going shopping on Saturday.
7 She's having lunch with her sister on Sunday morning.

7a

1 What are you doing this weekend?
2 Are you going to the cinema tomorrow?
3 What are your friends doing tonight?
4 Where are you going on Sunday?

12c (page 96)

1

1 b   2 a

2

Speaker 1:
1 She goes to the country.
2 She goes with friends.
3 She did a painting course.
4 She's doing a yoga course.

Speaker 2:
1 He goes to an adventure centre.
2 He sometimes goes with friends and he sometimes goes alone.
3 He went canoeing.
4 He's going mountain climbing.

3
1 behind   2 under   3 on   4 between

4
1 works   2 's meeting   3 went   4 read
5 're going   6 goes

5a
1 What do you do?
2 What are you doing?
3 What do you usually do at the weekend?
4 What did you do last weekend?
5 What are you doing this weekend?

12d (page 97)

1
1 next   2 in   3 at   4 tomorrow   5 in   6 on   7 at   8 on

2
1 Would you   2 Do you   3 I can't   4 do you
5 I'd   6 Would you

12e (page 98)

1
1 Francesca, Dani
2 Dani, Francesca

2a
1 put   2 come

2b
1 b   2 c   3 d   4 a

2c

	Present continuous	Present simple (he/she/it)	Past simple
arrive	arriving	arrives	arrived
come	coming	comes	came
do	doing	does	did
drive	driving	drives	drove
fly	flying	flies	flew
get	getting	gets	got
have	having	has	had
leave	leaving	leaves	left
lie	lying	lies	lay
make	making	makes	made
move	moving	moves	moved
phone	phoning	phones	phoned
run	running	runs	ran
see	seeing	sees	saw
sit	sitting	sits	sat
smile	smiling	smiles	smiled
study	studying	studies	studied
swim	swimming	swims	swam
travel	travelling	travels	travelled
work	working	works	worked

3
1 a, e   2 d, h   3 c, f   4 b, g

4
Example answer:
Dear Eve
Thanks for the DVDs. They were really interesting. I watched the first one last night and the second one this morning!
Thanks again. Speak to you soon.
Love,
Rachel

Learning skills / Check! (page 99)

3
1 newspaper   2 ironing   3 window   4 builder
5 motorbike

IELTS practice test

Listening
1 C when you go to do your test, please go to room 16
2 A Your English test only takes one hour and ten minutes.
3 32 (years old) I am thirty-two years old.
4 Manchester I was born in Manchester.
5 yes My wife's name is Helen. We got married three years ago.
6 22 West Street My address is 22 West Street.
7 golf my favourite sport is golf
8 Spanish I studied Spanish at school
9 Italian I can also speak Italian
10 (fried) chicken my favourite food is fried chicken
11 C That leaves Thursday. I hope that's a good day for everyone.
12 C To catch the bus, please come to the college no later than seven forty-five.
13 A In a student group, we only pay £12 each.
14 B/D We can sit and eat ... together in the garden
15 D/B There are lots of lovely things in the gift shop.
16 German see the work of German artists
17 (old) books a fantastic collection of old English books
18 Yellow (Room) that's the Yellow Room
19 Russian The maps are on loan from a Russian museum.
20 clothes you can see some clothes that people wore
21 September we like to go in September
22 bicycle We go everywhere by bicycle.
23 B I choose where we go and which route we take.
24 A when it comes to booking hotels, ... Anna does that
25 C we talk about it and decide together
26 A Anna likes to have a break. She tells me when it's time to stop for a rest.
27 A I answer any calls and texts we get.
28 B Anna hates shopping. So ... I go into the shops.
29 A photos ... I take lots of them on my phone
30 C we take turns to do that. I do it one day and Anna does it the next.
31 Asia There are also a few in Asia.
32 15 In the wild, lions usually live for about fifteen years.
33 5 ... usually there are as many as five born at the same time
34 20 resting – twenty hours a day is not unusual
35 male The male lion always starts the meal.
36 rugby in the UK and Ireland, one of the most famous rugby teams is called ...
37 soccer/football there is a soccer team called ...
38 South Africa one of the most famous cricket teams in South Africa
39 Canada 'the Lac St Louis Lions' ice hockey team in Canada
40 basketball 'the Dublin Lions' in Ireland. They play basketball.

Reading

1 D Open every day from 19.00
2 E international menu
3 A Famous for its excellent seafood
4 E Famous for its vegetable curry
5 B Very low prices
6 F Enjoy a relaxing meal in peaceful surroundings
7 E Open Tuesday to Sunday
8 C No cheques or credit cards accepted
9 C Popular with office workers at lunchtime
10 B Live band in the evening at weekends
11 vii on Norman Street ... just a few minutes' walk from the train station. The number 4A bus stops outside
12 i English language classes ... learn how to do jobs like hairdressing, motor-vehicle maintenance and hotel work
13 v residential accommodation ... self-catering apartments
14 ii gym and fitness centre ... tennis courts ... football teams
15 ix If you'd like to study ... an application form ... Enrolment Officer
16 vi employer ... working at the college
17 D I don't serve their meals
18 C I usually work an eight-hour shift
19 A I hold a computer club for students
20 B I drove a police car
21 B eighteen weeks' basic training at police college
22 C degree course in science at university ... and a year at a teacher training college
23 B would like to become a police inspector one day
24 A wait for their time to go ... When they come back
25 C there are not always simple answers
26 A a three-year diploma
27 B interview them and take notes
28 surgical ward
29 (to/the/a) court
30 www.canteach.gov.uk
31 NOT GIVEN
32 TRUE Billy lives ... with his wife, Linda. They were married ten years ago.
33 FALSE Billy worked in an office ... He hated his job.
34 NOT GIVEN
35 FALSE Linda has an office in their home and she works there.
36 FALSE he doesn't play golf very much
37 TRUE he works at golf courses now
38 computers Billy worked in an office in New York. He worked with computers.
39 lakes Billy dives in the lakes for these golf balls.
40 lost She sells the lost golf balls that Billy finds.